Anatomy and Physiology
Section A

Third Edition

Student Guide

Written by

Robert Hilley

Project coordinated by

Cheryl Dorris

Developed by

MAVCC
1500 West Seventh Avenue
Stillwater, Oklahoma 74074-4364

©2015

Printed in the United States of America by the
Oklahoma Department of Career and Technology Education
Stillwater, OK 74074-4364

For more information, contact

MAVCC
1500 West Seventh Avenue
Stillwater, OK 74074-4364

Internet: www.mavcc.com
Phone: 800.654.3988

Table of Contents

Modules of Instruction

Glossary

SECTION A:
Introduction to Anatomy and Physiology

Module 1-A: Organization of the Human Body

Module Contents

PREREQUISITES:
None

Learning Activities Sheet

Student name _____

DIRECTIONS

Place a checkmark in the appropriate box as you complete each of the steps below.

❑ 1. **Take** Pretest provided by your instructor.

❑ 2. **Stop** Have your instructor evaluate your performance. Follow your instructor's recommendations concerning the following learning activities.

❑ 3. **Read** Module Objective Sheet.

❑ 4. **Study** Information Sheet, Objectives 1 through 14.

❑ 5. **Research** Online resources to learn more about the organization of the human body. Your instructor will list several Web sites on the blanks below. Visit at least three of the following Web sites.

- _____
- _____
- _____
- _____
- _____
- _____
- _____

❑ 6. **Do** Assignment Sheet 1, "Practice Critical Thinking: Use Directional Terms to Describe Surgical Incisions."

❑ 7. **Stop** Have your instructor evaluate your performance. If the evaluation is satisfactory, continue to step 8. If the evaluation is not satisfactory, repeat step 6.

❑ 8. **Study** Student Supplement 1, "Anatomy and Physiology Terms," and Student Supplement 2, "Anatomical Terms."

❑ 9. **Do** Assignment Sheet 2, "Define Medical Terms."

❑ 10. **Stop** Have your instructor evaluate your performance. If the evaluation is satisfactory, continue to step 11. If the evaluation is not satisfactory, repeat steps 8 and 9.

❏ 11. **Do** Assignment Sheet 3, "Construct a Model of an Organ of the Human Body."

❏ 12. **Stop** Have your instructor evaluate your performance. If the evaluation is satisfactory, continue to step 13. If the evaluation is not satisfactory, repeat step 11.

❏ 13. **Take** Written Test provided by your instructor.

❏ 14. **Stop** Have your instructor evaluate your performance. If the evaluation is satisfactory, continue to step 15. If the evaluation is not satisfactory, repeat step 4.

❏ 15. **Check** With your instructor for any additional assignments to be completed.

❏ 16. **Do** Additional assignments your instructor lists below.

_____

_____

_____

❏ 17. **Take** Module Review provided by your instructor.

❏ 18. **Stop** Have your instructor evaluate your performance. Follow your instructor's recommendations concerning a review of the above learning activities.

❏ 19 **Stop** Have your instructor evaluate your performance on this module by compiling your scores on the Written Test, assignment sheets, and Module Review. If the evaluation is satisfactory, proceed to the next module. If the evaluation is not satisfactory, ask your instructor for further instructions.

*Permission to duplicate this Learning Activities Sheet is granted.

Module Objective Sheet

MODULE OBJECTIVE

After completing this module, you should be able to use anatomical terms to identify the general regions of the body, name the major body structures, and list the major organs and structures in the major organ systems. You should demonstrate these competencies by completing the assignment sheets and by scoring a minimum of 85 percent on the Written Test and on the Module Review.

SPECIFIC OBJECTIVES

After completing this module, you should be able to:

1. Define the terms *anatomy* and *physiology*.

2. Define the term *anatomical position*.

3. Label the common body planes.

4. Match the directional terms used in anatomy to their descriptions.

5. Describe the locating terms used in anatomy.

6. Describe the body positions.

7. List the general regions of the body.

8. State the contents of the major body cavities.

9. Label the quadrants of the abdominopelvic cavity.

10. Match the major abdominopelvic organs to their quadrant locations.

11. Label the regions of the abdomen.

12. List the major body structures in order of increasing complexity.

13. Match the major organ systems to their functions.

14. List the major organs and structures in each of the major organ systems.

15. Practice critical thinking: use directional terms to describe surgical incisions. (Assignment Sheet 1)

16. Define medical terms. (Assignment Sheet 2)

17. Construct a model of an organ of the human body. (Assignment Sheet 3)

Information Sheet

OBJECTIVE 1

The terms *anatomy* and *physiology*

KEY TERMS

Organ (or´-guhn)—A special structure within the body that is arranged in an organized manner to perform a specific function

Organism (or´-guh-niz-uhm)—A living person, animal, or plant

a. Anatomy (uh-nat´-uh-me)—The scientific study of the structure of an **organism** that describes the size, shape, construction, and relative positions of the **organs** in the body

b. Physiology (fiz-e-awl´-uh-je)—The scientific study of the functions of an organism that describes how the organs work independently and in relation to the whole organism

✔ **Note:** A key to success in the medical profession is an understanding of how the human body is structured and how its parts function individually and together.

OBJECTIVE 2

The term *anatomical position*

a. Anatomical (an-uh-tawm´-i-kuhl) position—A position of the body in which a person stands erect, facing directly forward, feet pointed forward and slightly apart, arms hanging down at the sides with the palms facing forward; a standard method of viewing the body so that the anatomy can be consistently described

✔ **Note:** Figures 1 through 3 on the next page show a person posed in anatomical position. Three standard views provide perspectives of the anatomical position: anterior (ventral, front) view, lateral (side) view, and posterior (dorsal, back) view.

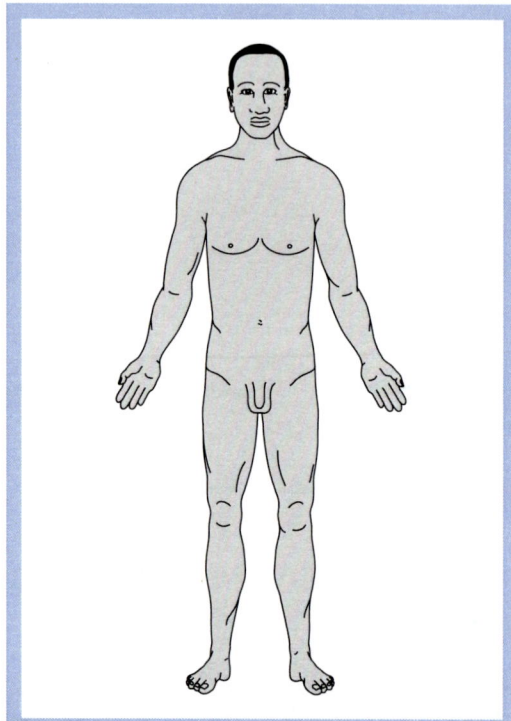

Figure 1
Anatomical position: Anterior view

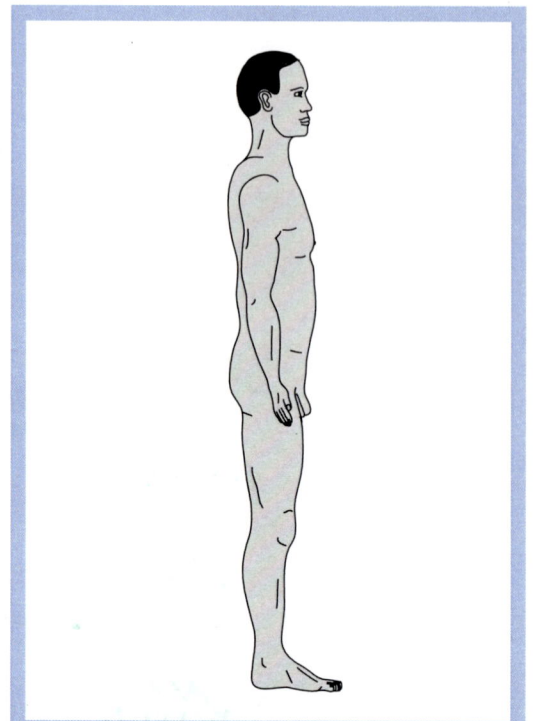

Figure 2
Anatomical position: Lateral view

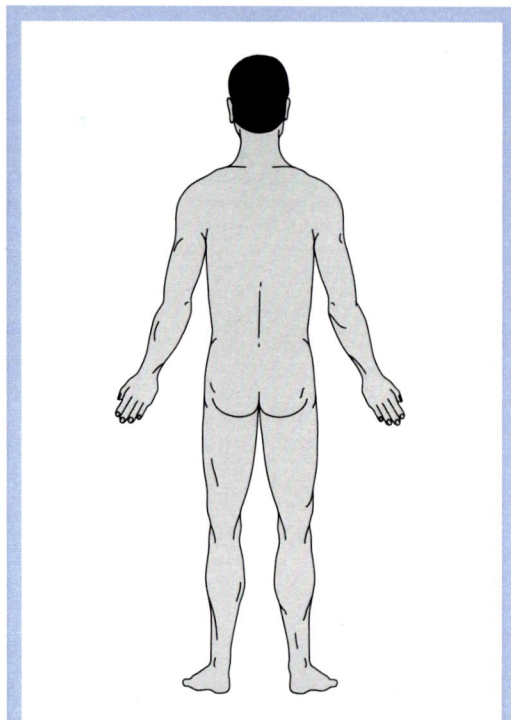

Figure 3
Anatomical position: Posterior view

OBJECTIVE 3	**Common body planes**

✔ **Note:** Because anatomy and physiology deal with internal as well as external features of the body, it is helpful to be able to describe the internal views of the body, as if the body were divided into parts. These views are referred to as *planes* and can be thought of as a straight slice through the body at a particular angle relative to anatomical position. Figures 4 through 8 illustrate the five common body planes: (1) median plane, (2) sagittal plane, (3) coronal plane, (4) transverse plane, and (5) oblique plane.

a. Median plane (med´-e-uhn plan´)—A lengthwise plane running through the midline of the body from front to back and dividing the body into equal right and left halves

✔ **Note:** The median plane is also referred to as the *midline plane* or *midsagittal plane.*

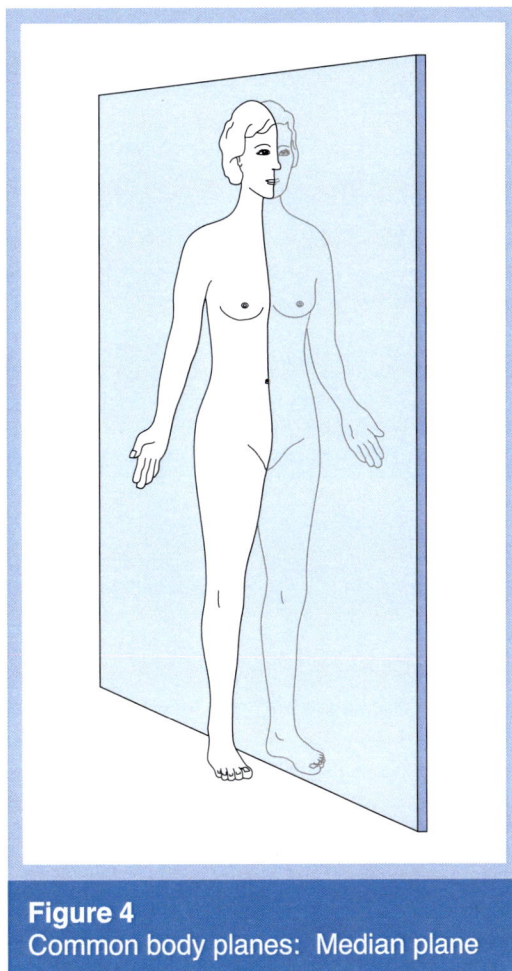

Figure 4
Common body planes: Median plane

b. Sagittal (saj´-uht-uhl) plane—A lengthwise plane running parallel to the median plane but not through the midline and dividing the body into unequal left and right parts

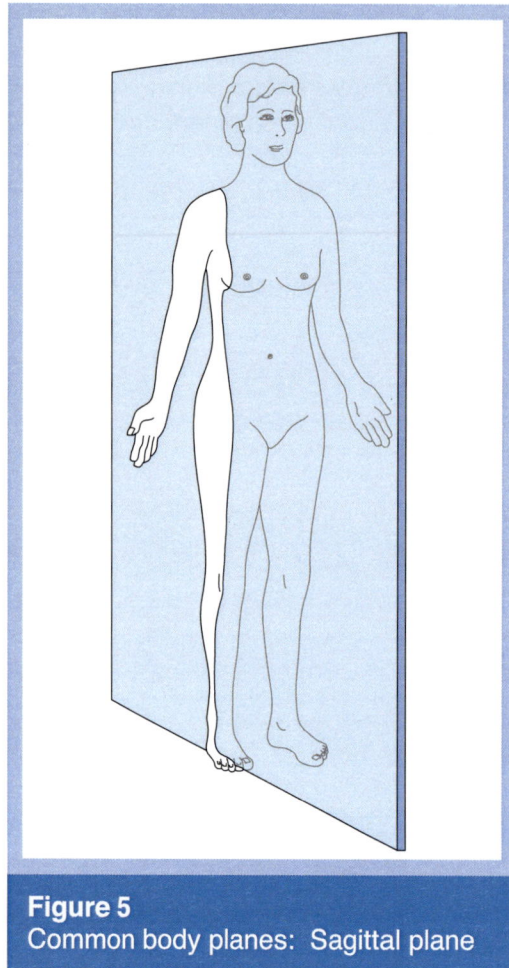

Figure 5
Common body planes: Sagittal plane

c. Coronal (kuh-ron´-uhl) plane—A lengthwise plane running from side to side and dividing the body into front and back parts

> ✔ **Note:** A coronal plane is also called a *frontal plane*. A coronal plane that passes through an organ creates a longitudinal section of the organ.

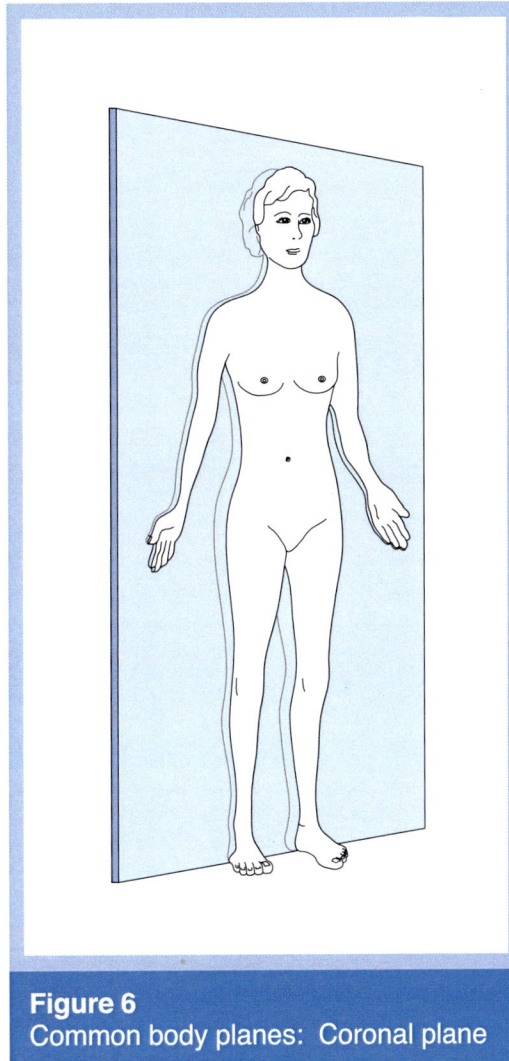

Figure 6
Common body planes: Coronal plane

d. Transverse (tranz´-vuhrs) plane—A horizontal plane passing through the body from front to back and dividing the body into equal upper and lower parts

✔ **Note:** A transverse plane is also called a *horizontal plane* or *cross-sectional plane*. A transverse plane passing through an organ creates a cross section of the organ.

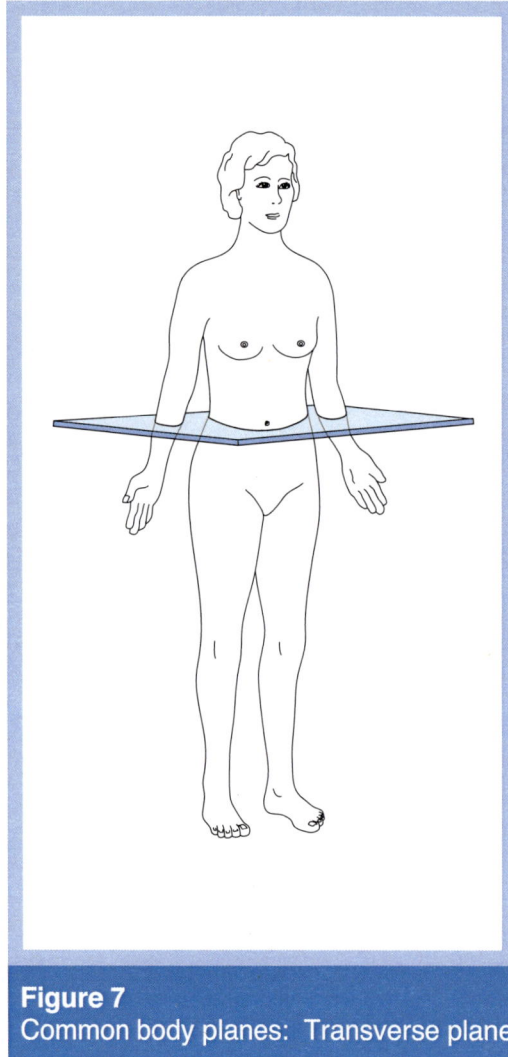

Figure 7
Common body planes: Transverse plane

e. Oblique (o-blek´) plane—A lengthwise plane passing through the body at a 45-degree angle to a sagittal plane or to the median plane

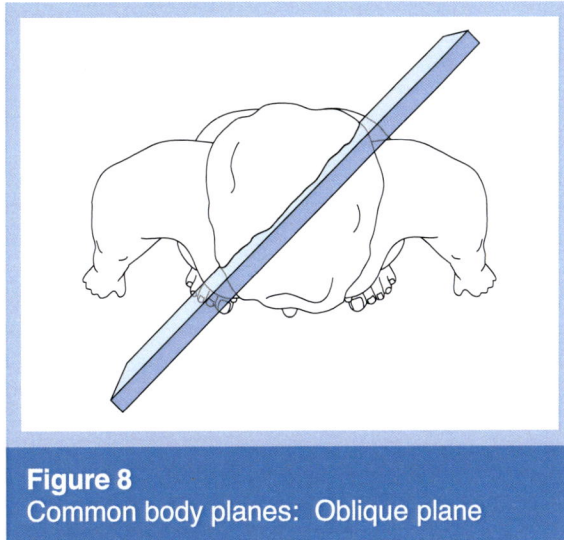

Figure 8
Common body planes: Oblique plane

OBJECTIVE 4

Directional terms used in anatomy

✔ **Note:** Medical personnel often must indicate the location of anatomical features, such as tumors or injuries. The easiest way of describing such locations is to refer to them in relation to a fixed body part. The following terms are commonly used to describe an anatomical position in relation to body parts. Figure 9 illustrates many of these directional terms.

a. Superior (su-pir´-e-uhr)—More toward the head

Example: The knee is superior to the ankle.

✔ **Note:** Another term for superior is *cephalic*.

b. Inferior (in-fir´-e-uhr)—Farther from the head

Example: The wrist is inferior to the elbow.

✔ **Note:** Another term for inferior is *caudal*.

c. Anterior (an-tir´-e-uhr)—More toward the front of the body

Example: The nose is anterior to the ears.

✔ **Note:** Another term for anterior is *ventral*.

d. Posterior (paw-stir´-e-uhr)—More toward the backside of the body

Example: The heel is posterior to the toes.

✔ **Note:** Another term for posterior is *dorsal*.

e. Proximal (prawk´-suh-muhl)—Nearer to a point of reference

Example: The neck is proximal to the head as compared to the stomach.

f. Distal (dis´-tuhl)—Farther from a point of reference

Example: The elbow is distal to the hand as compared to the wrist.

g. Medial (med´-e-uhl)—Closer to the midline of the body

Example: The eyes are medial as compared to the ears.

h. Lateral (lat´-uh-ruhl)—Farther from the midline of the body

Example: The hips are lateral as compared to the navel.

i. Internal (in-tuhrn´-uhl)—Below the surface

Example: The heart and lungs are internal.

j Exterior (ek-stir´-e-uhr)—On the surface

Example: The skin is exterior.

k. Deep (dep´)—Away from the surface

Example: The kidneys are deep.

l. Superficial (su-puhr-fish´-uhl)—Near the surface

Example: A rash of the skin is superficial.

m. Central (sen´-truhl)—At or near the middle

Example: The nose is central on the face.

n. Peripheral (puh-rif´-uh-ruhl)—At or near the edge

Example: The toes are peripheral to the foot.

o. Parietal (puh-ri´-uht-uhl)—At the wall of a body cavity

Example: The mucosa that line most body cavities are parietal.

p. Visceral (vis´-uh-ruhl)—Within a body cavity

Example: Most internal organs are visceral.

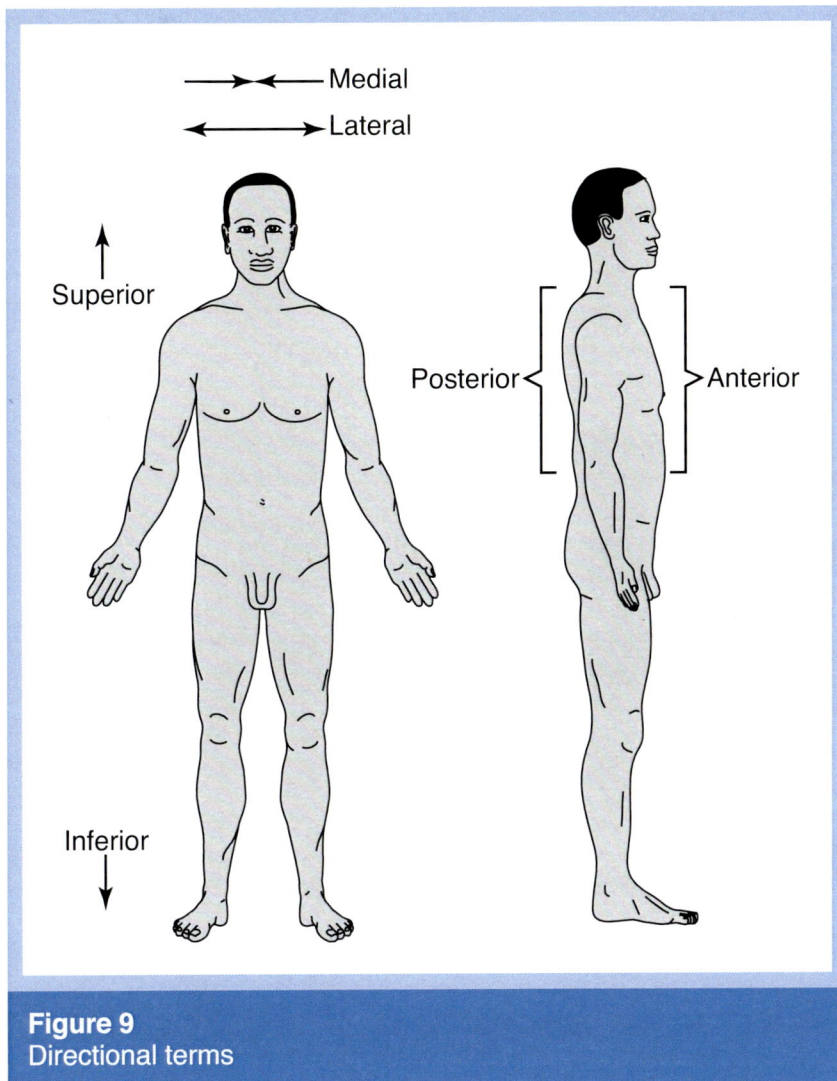

Figure 9
Directional terms

OBJECTIVE 5 | **Locating terms used in anatomy**

a.   Cephalic (suh-fal´-ik)—Referring to the head or to the head end of a structure

   ✔ **Note:** Another term for cephalic is *cranial* (kra´-ne-uhl).

b.   Caudal (kawd´-uhl)—Referring to the tail or tail end of a structure

c.   Palmar (pal´-muhr)—Referring to the palm of the hand

d.   Plantar (plant´-uhr)—Referring to the sole of the foot

e.   Greater curvature (grat´-uhr kuhr´-vuh-chuhr)—Referring to the outer and longer portion of a curved structure

f.   Lesser curvature (les´-uhr kuhr´-vuh-chuhr)—Referring to the inner and shorter portion of a curved structure

Module 1-A: Organization of the Human Body

| **Body positions**

KEY TERMS

Anesthetize (uh-nes´-thuh-tiz)—To create in a patient a loss of sensation, with or without a loss of consciousness; to create a condition of anesthesia (an-uhs-the´-zhuh) in a patient; to administer an anesthetic (an-uhs-thet´-ik)

Examination (ig-zam-uh-na´-shuhn)—An evaluation of a person's health based on appearance, the person's feelings and behavior, and the status of indicators of health such as temperature, blood pressure, and body chemistry

Surgery (sur´-juhre)—A medical procedure intended to correct physical defects, repair injuries, or treat diseases, especially through the use of medical instruments

✔ **Note:** There are many types of surgical procedures, or operations, performed for a number of diverse purposes. One of the principal reasons for studying anatomy and physiology is to assess the normal structure and functioning of the body in order to determine when surgery may be required and the nature of the procedure that might benefit the patient.

---

a. Erect (i-rekt´)—Standing or sitting upright

   ✔ **Note:** The erect position is used during portions of an **examination** and during procedures that do not require the patient to be fully **anesthetized**.

b. Supine (su-pin´)—Lying down face up

   ✔ **Note:** The supine position is sometimes referred to as the *dorsal recumbent* (ri-kuhm´-buhnt) *position*. Because recumbent means lying down, dorsal recumbent means lying on the back. This position is used during **surgeries** of the anterior anatomy, such as abdominal, pelvic, or facial surgery. For some procedures, such as delivery of a baby, the patient may be placed in a position with the head slightly raised in a position called the *semi-recumbent position*.

c. Prone (pron´)—Lying down on the stomach

   ✔ **Note:** The prone position is used to perform surgery on the posterior surface of the body, such as the back, the rectal area, and the posterior of the legs.

d. Lateral (lat´-uh-ruhl)—Lying on one side

   ✔ **Note:** The lateral position is used for surgeries that focus on a structure that is more to one side than to the middle. For example, a patient might be placed lateral on the left side if a surgery were to be performed on the right kidney. Most thoracic surgeries are performed in the lateral position.

| OBJECTIVE 7 | **General regions of the body** |

KEY TERMS

Fatal (fat´-uhl)—Resulting in death

Gland (gland´)—Any of the various structures within the body that produce specific chemicals to help with the functions of the body

✔ **Note:** There are glands in all parts of the body. You will study about them in relation to the systems that they support. Additionally, in a later module you will study a body system called the *endocrine* (en´-duh-kruhn) *system*, which consists primarily of glands and related structures.

Perineum (per-uh-ne´-uhm)—The area of tissue behind the pelvis that gives passage to the urinary and genital ducts and to the rectum

Vital organ (vit´-uhl or´-guhn)—An organ that must function properly in order for the life of the organism to continue

✔ **Note:** The heart, liver, and brain are vital organs. If these organs do not function properly, the person will die. Some organs are critical but not vital. For example, a person can live with one lung or one kidney. Other organs—the spleen and eyes for example—improve a person's ability to function but do not directly result in death if they stop functioning or are removed from the body.

a. Head

✔ **Note:** The head (see Figure 10) includes the area of the body above the neck, principally the cranium and face along with internal structures. Of obvious importance is the brain, but the head's internal structures also include the components of the mouth, nose, eyes, ears, as well as several **glands**.

b. Trunk

✔ **Note:** The trunk (see Figure 10) is also called the *torso* (tor´-so) and consists of what is commonly considered to be a person's body, excluding the head, arms, and legs. Thus, the trunk includes the neck, back, chest (thorax), abdomen, pelvis, and **perineum**. The majority of the **vital organs** are contained in the trunk.

c. Limbs

✔ **Note:** The limbs (see Figure 10), or *extremities* (ik-strem´-uht-ez), consist of the arms, legs, hands, and feet. They are important in movement but do not contain vital organs. Thus, a person may lose an extremity without it being **fatal**. However, due to the amount of blood that flows through the extremities, injury to an arm or leg can lead to bleeding that is severe enough to cause death.

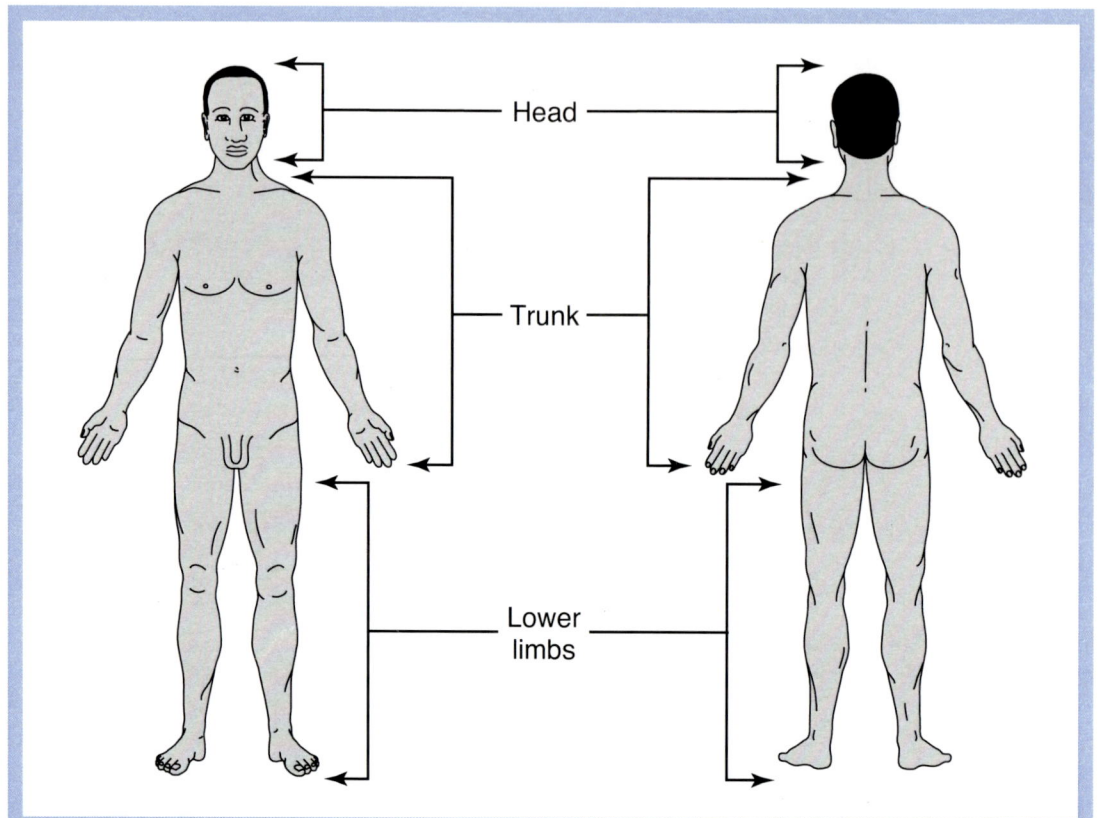

Figure 10
General regions of the body

OBJECTIVE 8	**Contents of the major body cavities**

✔ **Note:** The internal volume of the body is not solid. Under the framework formed by the skin, the muscles, and the skeleton are hollow areas called *cavities*. These cavities contain many of the organs and other structures that support life. Often the organs of a system will be contained within a single cavity. The information provided in this objective introduces you to the major body cavities and provides you with basic information about their contents. Some of the structures named will be familiar to you, while you may be less acquainted with others. At this point of your studies, you are not expected to have a thorough comprehension of the structure and functions of these organs—after all, the purpose of this course is to provide you with that knowledge. This objective and those that follow are intended to allow you to begin making these associations. The remainder of your studies will build on this foundation.

KEY TERM

System (sis´-tuhm)—A group of organs and related structures that work together to perform a common function

✔ **Note:** The functioning of the body is supported by a number of systems that perform specific purposes (see Objectives 13 and 14). Each system consists of one or more organs and additional structures that connect these organs and tie them to other systems.

---

a. Cranial (kra´-ne-uhl) cavity—Brain and pituitary gland

b. Spinal (spin´-uhl) cavity—Spinal cord

✔ **Note:** The cranial cavity and spinal cavity are sometimes referred to collectively as the *dorsal* (posterior or back) *cavity* (see Figure 11).

c. Pleural (plur´-uhl) cavities—One lung in each

d. Pericardial (per-uh-kard´-e-uhl) cavity—Heart

e. Mediastinal space (med-e-uh-stin´-uhl spas´)—Thymus gland, trachea, esophagus, bronchi, ends of the vena cavae, beginning of the aorta

✔ **Note:** The two pleural cavities, the pericardial cavity, and the mediastinal space are referred to collectively as the *thoracic cavity* (see Figure 11).

f. Abdominal (ab-dawm´-uhn-uhl) cavity—Stomach, liver, gallbladder, spleen, pancreas, most of the small and large intestines, kidneys

✔ **Note:** The abdominal cavity and the pelvic cavity are referred to collectively as the *abdominopelvic cavity*. The thoracic cavity (the cavity above the diaphragm) and the abdominopelvic cavity (the cavity below the diaphragm) are sometimes referred to collectively as the *ventral* (anterior or front) *cavity* (see Figure 11).

g. Pelvic (pel´-vik) cavity—Urinary bladder, sex organs, part of the large intestine, including the cecum, appendix, and rectum

✔ **Note:** The pelvic cavity roughly begins on a line along the level of the iliac crests.

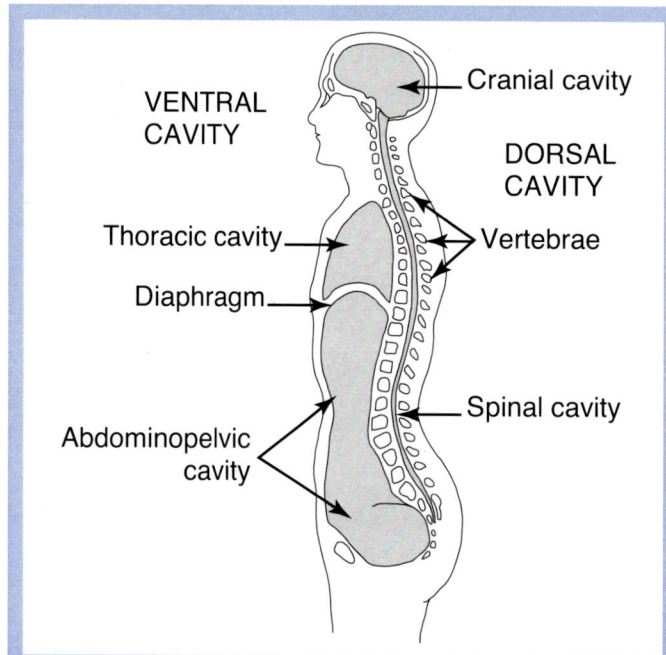

Figure 11
Major body cavities

OBJECTIVE 9

Quadrants of the abdominopelvic cavity

✔ **Note:** A quadrant is one-fourth of a given area. The external surface over the abdominopelvic cavity can be viewed in quadrants designated as upper and lower halves and right and left halves. This approach is convenient for indicating the location of the underlying organs and structures. For example, severe pain in the right lower quadrant may indicate appendicitis, an **inflammation** of the appendix, an extension to the large intestine. An important point to remember about how the quadrants are labeled is that left and right refer to the person's left and right sides. Thus, as you view a person with pain in the right lower quadrant, that location will be to your left.

KEY TERM

Inflammation (in-fluh-ma´-shuhn)—A group of reactions exhibited by tissue when exposed to irritants; the reactions may include swelling, heat, pain, and other signs of irritation

✔ **Note:** Indications such as heat, pain, and swelling (an enlargement of a body structure) are called *symptoms* (sim{p}´-tuhms). Symptoms can provide a great deal of information about a possible anatomical or physiological problem. The severity of the symptom and its location, whether the symptom is continuous or comes and goes, and the presence of other symptoms can help medical professionals assess a patient's condition and the effectiveness of treatment.

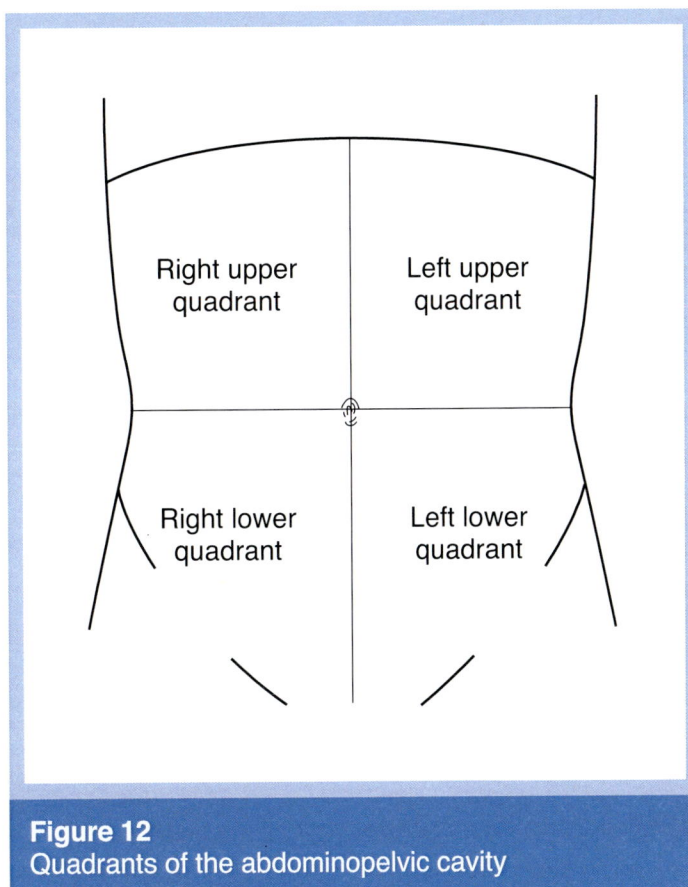

Right upper quadrant

Left upper quadrant

Right lower quadrant

Left lower quadrant

Figure 12
Quadrants of the abdominopelvic cavity

Module 1-A: Organization of the Human Body

Major abdominopelvic organs and their quadrant locations

a. Right upper quadrant (RUQ)

- Part of the small intestine, including the descending duodenum

- Upper ascending colon

- Most of the liver

- Gallbladder

- Bile ducts

- Head of the pancreas

- Right adrenal gland

- Right kidney

- Upper part of the right ureter

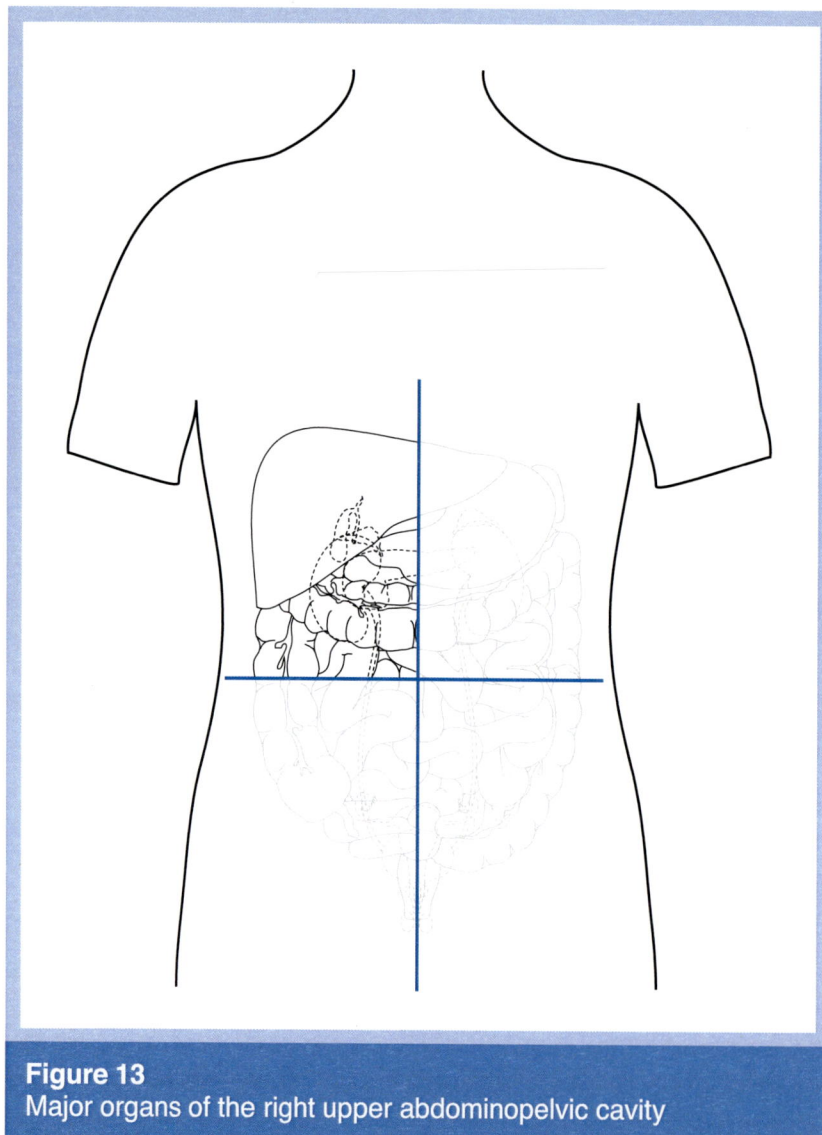

Figure 13
Major organs of the right upper abdominopelvic cavity

b.   Left upper quadrant (LUQ)

- Ascending part of the duodenum

- Upper descending colon

- Left half of the transverse colon

- Spleen

- Small part of the liver

- Left adrenal gland

- Left kidney

- Upper part of the left ureter

- Stomach

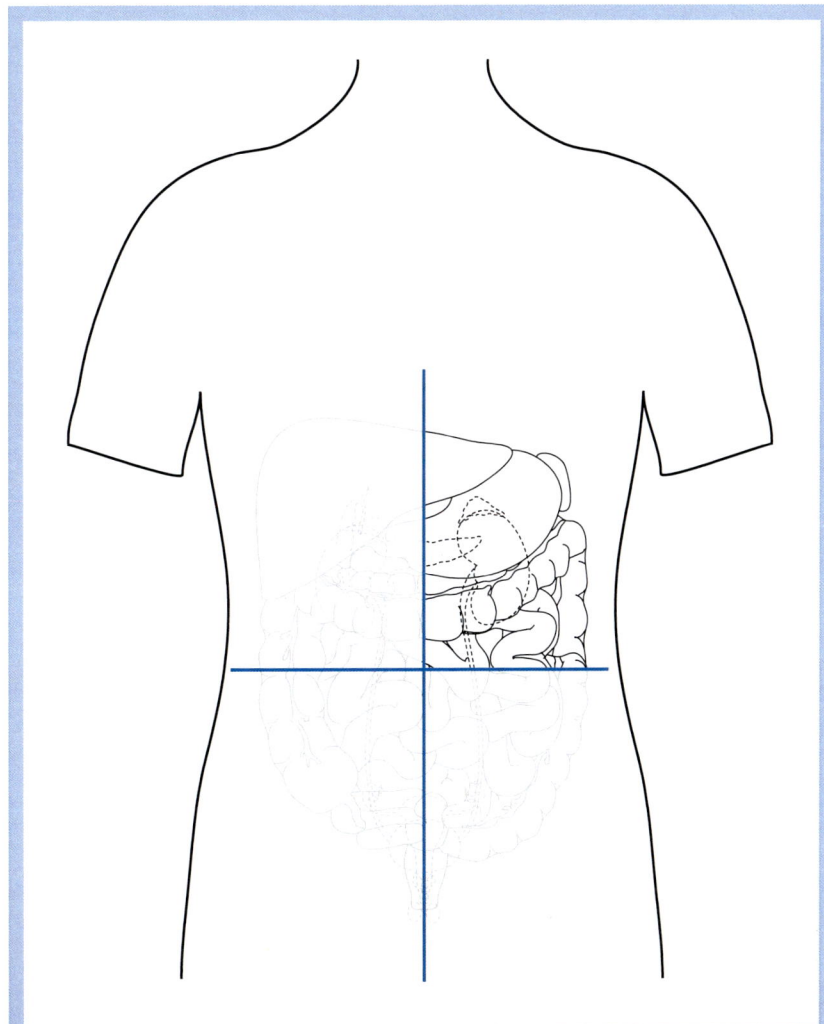

Figure 14
Major organs of the left upper abdominopelvic cavity

c. Right lower quadrant (RLQ)

- Lower ascending colon

- Cecum

- Appendi

- Lower right ureter

- Terminal ileum

- Part of the urinary bladder

- Sex organs

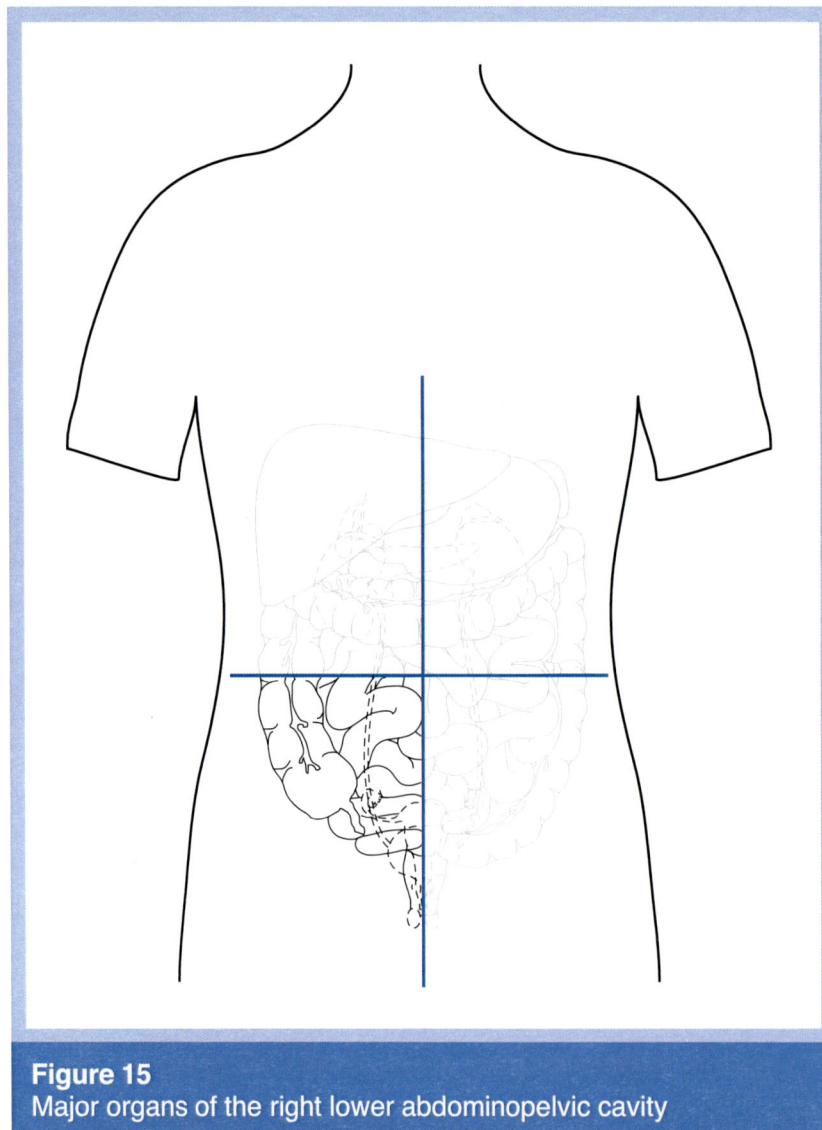

Figure 15
Major organs of the right lower abdominopelvic cavity

d.   Left lower quadrant (LLQ)

   •   Lower descending colon

   •   Small intestine (part of ileum)

   •   Part of the urinary bladder

   •   Sex organs

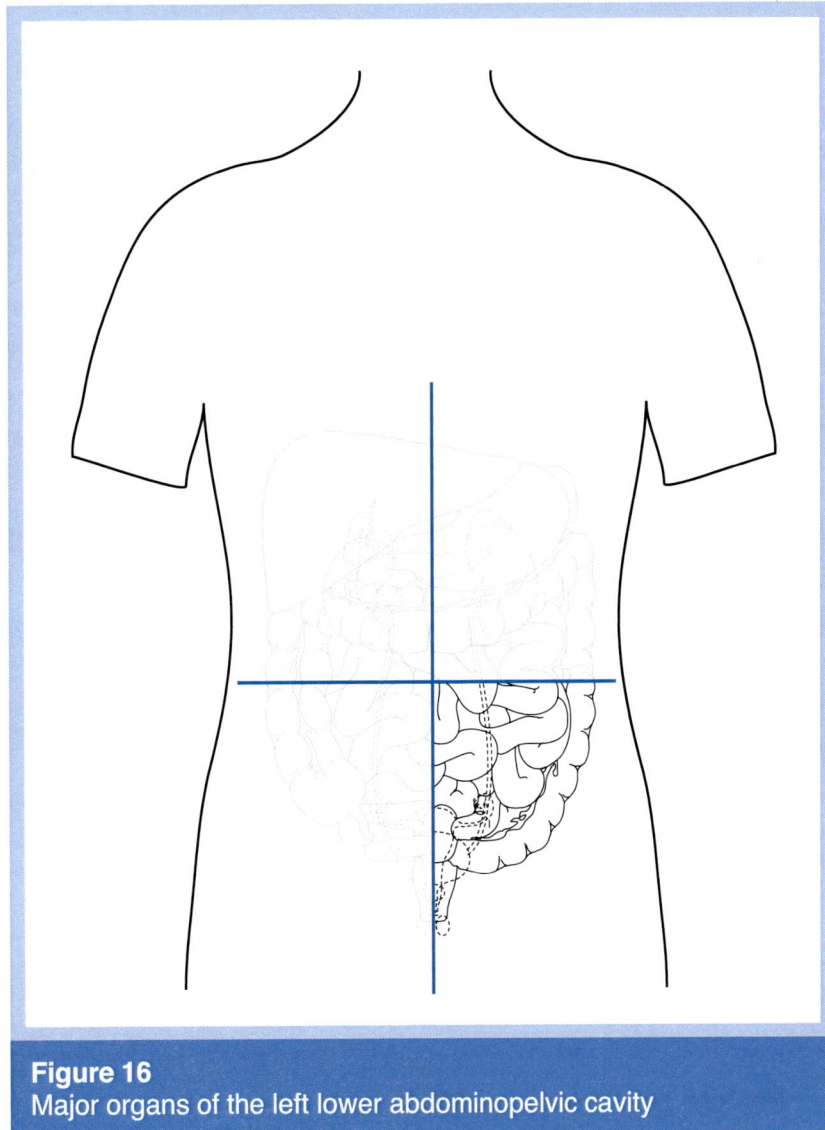

Figure 16
Major organs of the left lower abdominopelvic cavity

Module 1-A: Organization of the Human Body

OBJECTIVE 11	**Regions of the abdomen**

KEY TERMS

Cartilage (kart´-uhl-ij)—A type of body tissue that forms the skeleton of the developing fetus, most of which is converted to bone after birth

✔ **Note:** Some cartilaginous structures remain even in adults. These include structures in the nose and ears and on the joint surfaces of bones.

Umbilicus (uhm-buh-li´-kuhs)—The point at which the umbilical cord joined the fetus to the mother's womb during pregnancy; commonly referred to as the *navel* or *belly button*

✔ **Note:** The abdominal portion of the abdominopelvic region can be further divided into areas that allow more-precise identification of structures and symptoms. The nine regions of the abdomen (see Figure 17) are centered around the **umbilicus**. The area around the umbilicus is the center segment of the abdominal regions and is called the *umbilical region*. The area above it is called the *epigastric region*, from two Greek terms meaning "over the stomach." The area below the umbilical region is termed the *hypogastric* or "beneath the stomach" region. The areas to the left and right of the three medial regions are named for their locations relative to features of the skeleton. The upper sections lie over the lower ribs, below the rib cage, and are called *hypochondriac*, meaning "below the **cartilage**." The middle lateral regions are called the *lumbar regions* because they are anterior to the lumbar region of the back. Finally, the lower left and right regions lie over the hips and take the name of the hip bone, *iliac*.

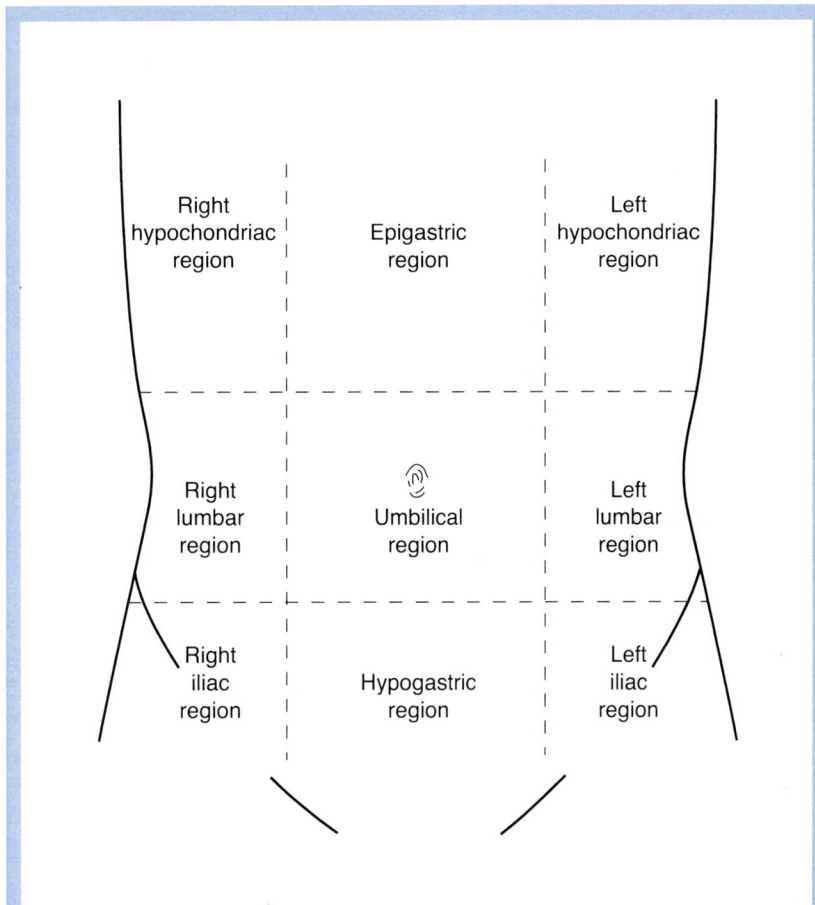

Figure 17
Nine regions of the abdomen

Module 1-A: Organization of the Human Body

OBJECTIVE 12 | **Major body structures in order of increasing complexity**

> KEY TERM
>
> **Structure** (struhk´-chuhr)—A part of the body, such as the heart, a bone, a gland, a cell, or a limb

✔ **Note:** Like all substances, the human body is composed of atoms, which in turn make molecules. Atoms and molecules form chemical elements and compounds. Certain combinations of chemicals exhibit the characteristic called *life*, which means that that combination of chemicals can move, grow, convert food into energy, and reproduce. The smallest bunches of chemicals that exhibit life are called *cells*. Cells include bacteria and organisms such as amoebas. All plants and animals, including humans, are made of cells. Cells form more-complex structures called *tissue*. Tissue can be organized to perform a specific function within a plant or animal. This organized structure is called an *organ*. Organs that work together in the performance of related functions are called *organ systems* or simply *systems*. The integrated systems thus make up the living creature called an *organism*.

a. Cell

b. Tissue

c. Organ

d. Organ system

e. Organism

OBJECTIVE 13 | **Major organ systems and their functions**

✔ **Note:** As you learned in Objective 8, a system is a group of organs and related structures that work together to perform a common function. The 12 major body systems and their functions in the body are presented below and are further discussed and illustrated in Objective 14.

a. Integumentary system (in-teg´-yuh-ment-uh-re sis´-tuhm)—Protects the organism from injury, disease, and infection; aids in the regulation of temperature, the excretion of wastes, and the reception of sensations

b. Skeletal (skel´-uht-uhl) system—Provides the framework for the body and works to protect and support the body

c. Muscular (muhs´-kyuh-luhr) system—Provides for body movement and support

d. Nervous (nuhr´-vuhs) system—Coordinates body activities by receiving, interpreting, and conducting messages to all the other systems of the body

e. Special senses (spesh´-uhl sens´-es)—Function in receiving sensations such as sight, smell, hearing, and taste

f.   Digestive (di-jes´-tiv) system—Receives, breaks down, and absorbs food substances and excretes waste products

g.   Circulatory (suhr´-kyuh-luh-tor-e) system—Transports materials throughout the body by carrying oxygen and nutrients in the blood to all the cells of the body and carrying away the waste products of the cells

h.   Respiratory (res´-puh-ruh-tor-e) system—Takes in oxygen from the air and gives off carbon dioxide, which is produced by cell metabolism

i.   Urinary (yur´-uh-ner-e) system—Serves in removing waste products from the blood and in excreting wastes in the form of urine

j.   Reproductive (re-pruh-duhk´-tiv) system—Involved with reproduction and childbirth

k.   Endocrine (en´-duh-kruhn) system—Serves to regulate various body functions through glands that secrete hormones directly into the blood to slow down or increase the activity of the cells

l.   Immune (im-yun´) system—Provides protection against disease and infection

OBJECTIVE 14   **Major organs and structures in each of the major organ systems**

a.   Integumentary system—Skin, hair, nails, duct glands (see Figure 18)

b.   Skeletal system—Bones, joints, cartilage, connective tissue (see Figure 19)

c.   Muscular system—Skeletal, smooth, and cardiac muscles (see Figure 20)

d.   Nervous system—Brain, spinal cord, peripheral nerves (see Figure 21)

e.   Special senses—Eyes, ears, nose, taste buds (see Figure 22)

f.   Digestive system—Mouth, pharynx, esophagus, stomach, large and small intestines, accessory organs such as the gallbladder and pancreas (see Figure 23)

g.   Circulatory system—Heart, blood vessels, blood, lymphatic tissues (see Figures 24-a and 24-b)

h.   Respiratory system—Lungs, nose, pharynx, larynx, trachea (see Figure 25)

i.   Urinary system—Kidneys, ureter, bladder, urethra (see Figure 26)

j.   Reproductive system—Sex organs and ducts to the outside (see Figures 27-a and 27-b)

k.   Endocrine system—Ductless glands (see Figure 28)

Examples: Thyroid, pituitary

l.   Immune system—White blood cells, antibodies

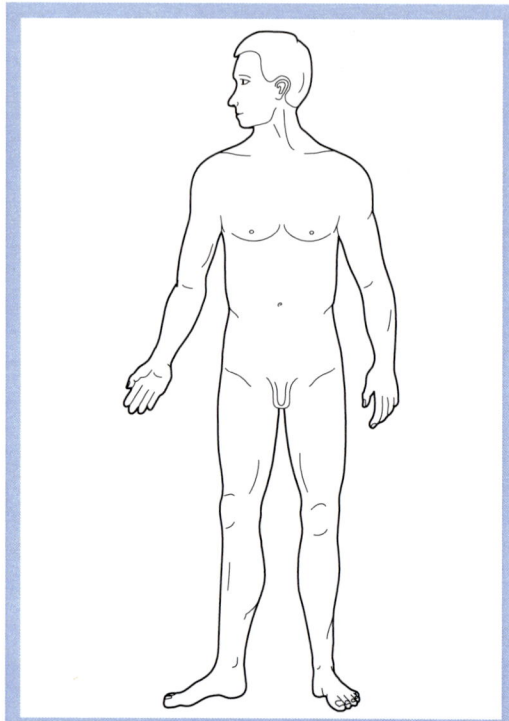

Figure 18
Integumentary system

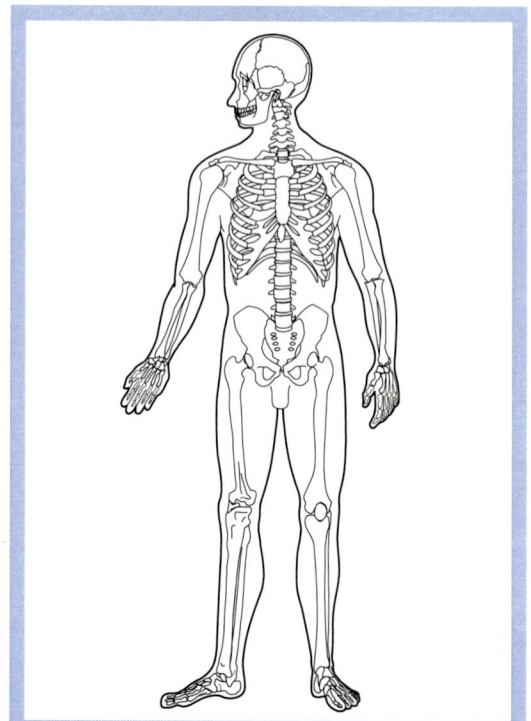

Figure 19
Skeletal system

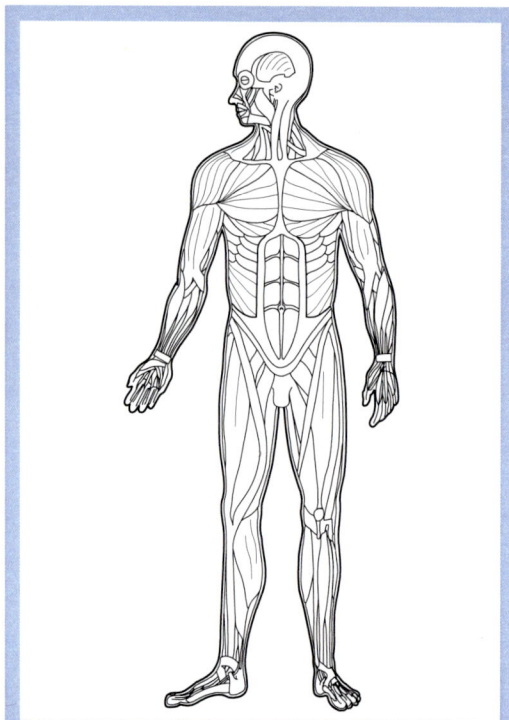

Figure 20
Muscular system

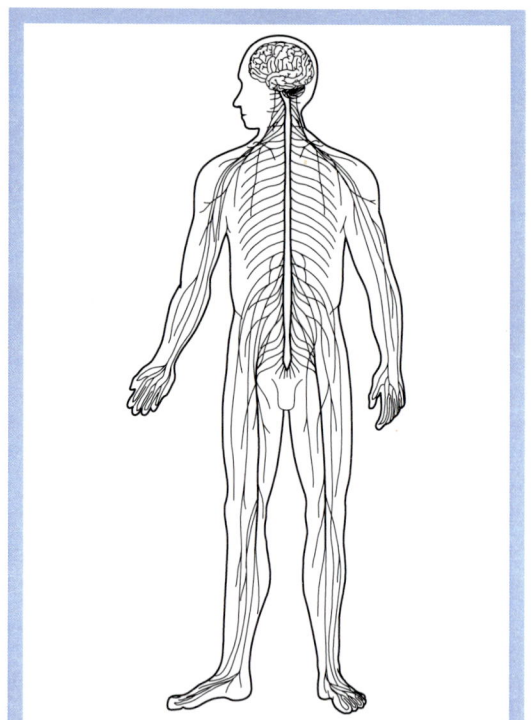

Figure 21
Nervous system

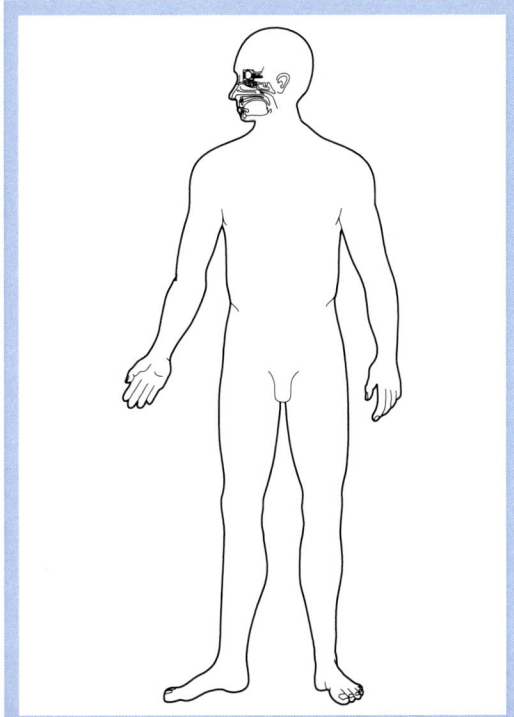

Figure 22
Special senses

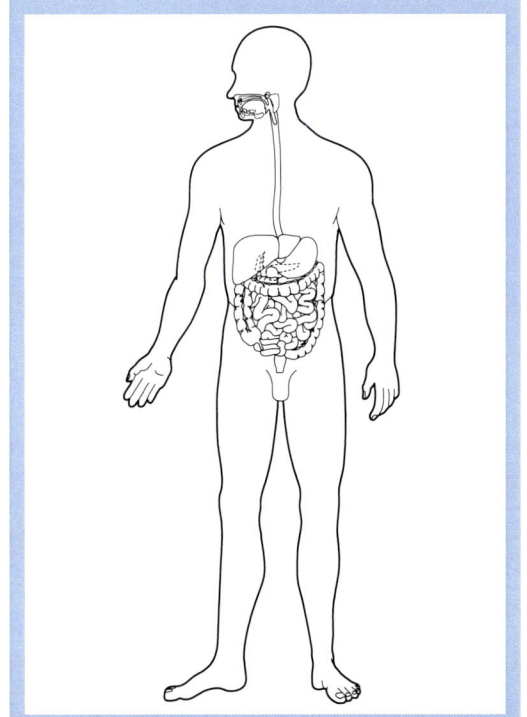

Figure 23
Digestive system

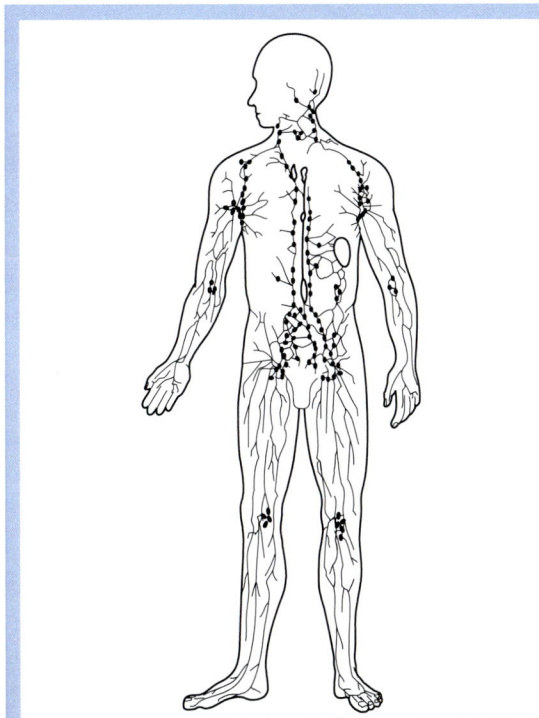

Figure 24-a
Circulatory system (lymphatic)

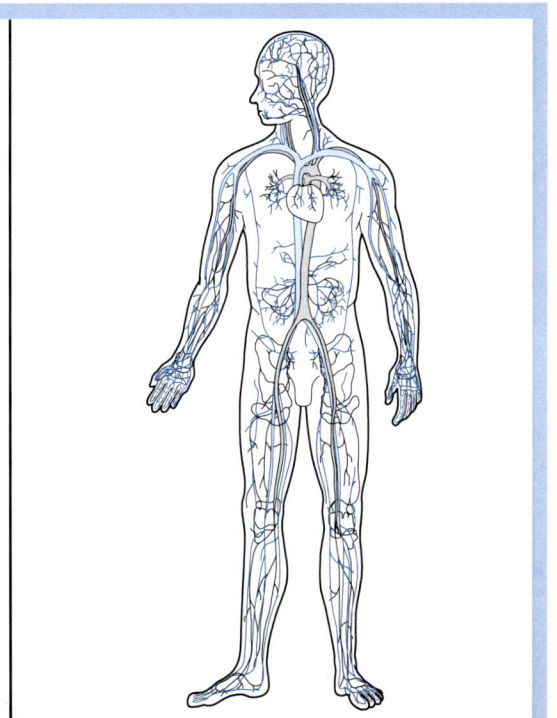

Figure 24-b
Circulatory system (blood)

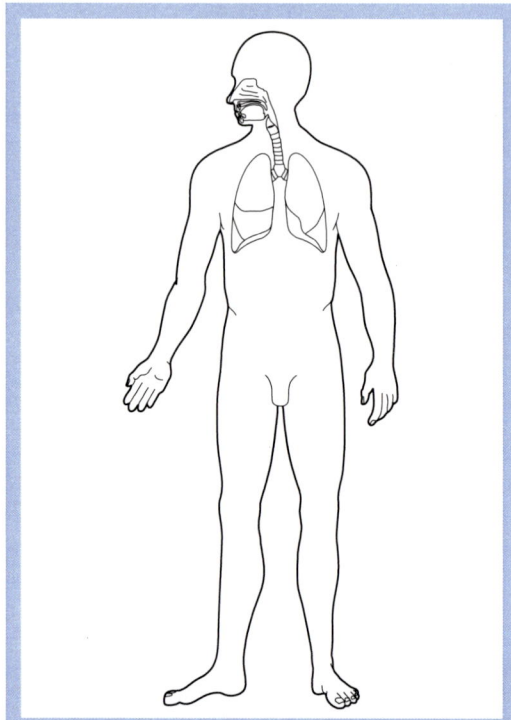

Figure 25
Respiratory system

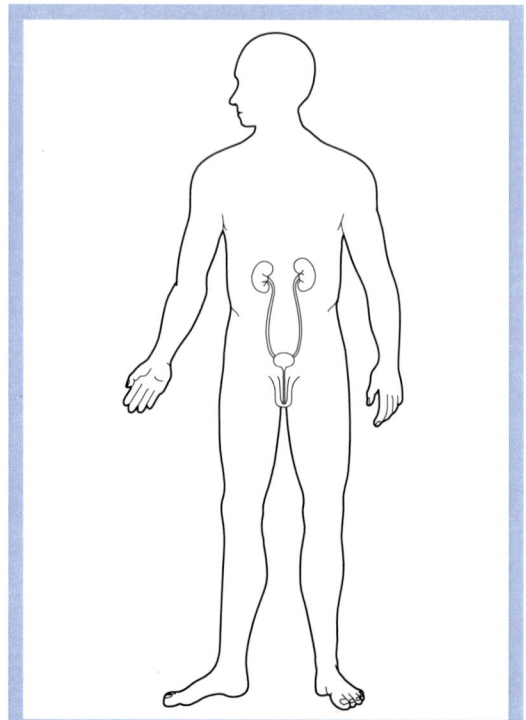

Figure 26
Urinary system

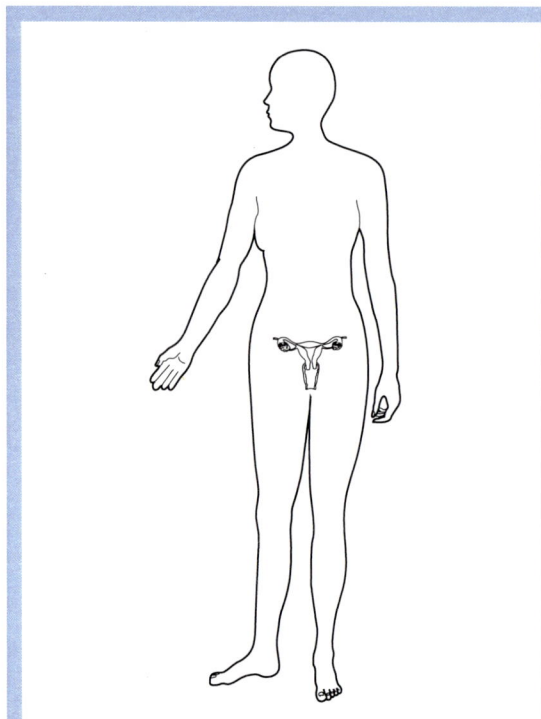

Figure 27-a
Reproductive system (female)

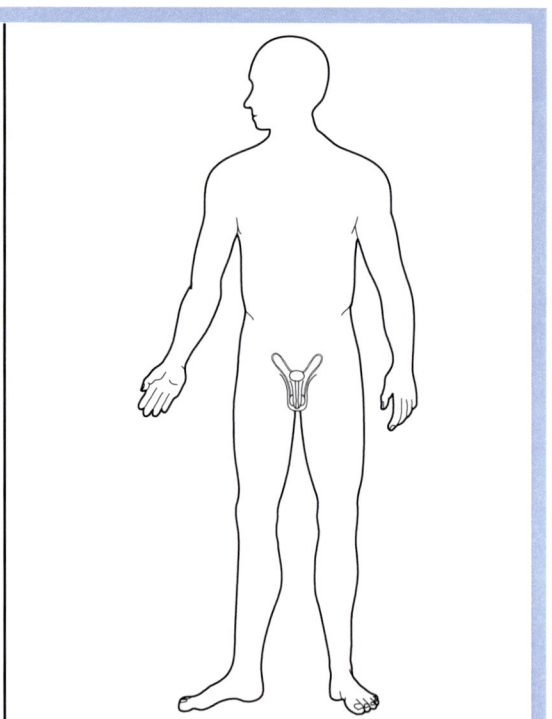

Figure 27-b
Reproductive system (male)

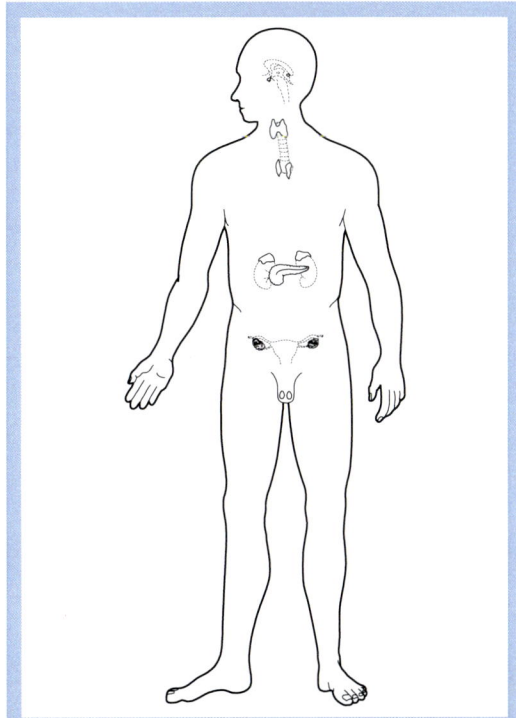

Figure 28
Endocrine system

Student Supplement 1—Anatomy and Physiology Terms

INTRODUCTION

You have learned that anatomy and physiology are the studies of body structures and functions. For the most part, the words used to name body parts are simply descriptions of structure and function. Many of these names describe a body part or its function and indicate its location or relationship to other body parts. But you may not always recognize these terms because many of them are based on foreign words, often Latin. Once you have learned a few key terms, you will be able to decipher the meaning of words that you have never seen.

This student supplement presents a number of terms, many of which you encountered in this module. The table on pages 37 and 38 lists these words, explains important terms and prefixes and suffixes, and provides more words that you will come across in your studies. Prefixes are stems on the front of a word, while suffixes end words. For example, *ascending* is a word that is used in anatomy, as in *ascending colon*. *Ascending* consists of a prefix (a-), a root word (-scend-), and a suffix (-ing). *A-* comes from a Latin word meaning "up" or "out of," while *scend* comes from a Latin word that means "climb." The *-ing* ending is a common English suffix to show an action or process. Thus, *ascending* describes the fact that this section of the colon makes an upward turn.

Study the terms in this student supplement to help you become familiar with the vocabulary of anatomy and physiology. Use the table of terms as a reference as you continue your studies.

Table 1
Anatomy and Physiology Terms

Application	Term/prefix/suffix	Refers to	Related words
body parts and areas	abdomen	the area between the chest and hips	abdominal, abdominopelvic
	caudal	a tail	cauda equina (literally, *horse's tail*, a branch of nerves)
	cephalic	the head	encephalitis, cephalic vein
	cerebrum	the brain	cerebral cortex, cerebrospinal fluid
	cranial	the head or skull	cranium, craniosacral
	corona	a circle (from Latin for *crown*)	coronary artery, coronal suture
	hemoglobin	a substance in blood (the prefix *hemo-* or *hema-* indicates blood)	hemorrhage, hemophilia, hemorrhoid, hematuria
	hepatic	the liver	hepatic artery, hepatic jaundice, hepatitis
	iliac	a hip	iliac crest, ilium, sacroiliac joint
	lumbar	the lower back	lumbar vertebra, lumbar plexus
	nasal	the nose	nasal septum, nasopharynx
	neuron	a portion of nerve	neuroglia, neuromuscular junction, neurotoxin
	ocular	an eye	occulomotor nerve, orbicularis oculi muscle
	optic	an eye	optic nerve, optic chiasma, myopia
	oral	the mouth	oral cavity, oropharynx
	os	bone	ossification, osteoporosis
	parietal	the wall of a body cavity	parietal lobe, parietal pericardium
	pelvis	the hips	pelvic inlet, abdominopelvic
	pleural	the chest cavity	pleural membrane, pleurisy
	pulmonar	the lungs	pulmonary circulation, cardiopulmonary resuscitation
	rectum	lower end of intestines	rectal fold, rectal thermometer
	renal	the kidneys	renal failure, renal medulla
	sinus	an opening	maxillary sinus, sinusoids
	thora	the chest	thoracic duct, thoracolumbar
	umbilical	the navel	umbilical cord, umbilicus
	urinary	the tract for eliminating urine	ureter, urethra, urea, urinary bladder
	visceral	the organs within a cavity	visceral peritoneum, visceral pleura
directions	ascending	rising up	ascending colon, ascending aorta
	descending	going down	descending colon, descending tract
	distal	farther from the origin	distal convoluted tubule
	dorsal	toward the back	dorsal arch, dorsal cavity, dorsal root
	internal	within	internal carotid artery
	lateral	away from the midline	lateral ventricle, lateral rectus muscle
	peripheral	extending from	peripheral nervous system
	proximal	closer to the origin	proximal convoluted tubule
	sagittal	cut in a straight line (from Latin for *arrow*)	sagittal plane, sagittal suture
	transverse	across	transverse colon, transverse sinus
	ventral	toward the front	ventral cavity, ventral root
comparisons	ante-	before	anterior
	anti-	against, opposing	antibody, antitoxin, antiseptic
	ecto-	outside	ectoderm
	endo-	within	endothelium
	epi-	on, over	epidermis, epigastric
	ex-	out of	external, excrete
	homo-, homeo-	same, unchanged	homeostasis, homozygous

Table 1 (cont.)
Anatomy and Physiology Terms

Application	Term/prefix/suffix	Refers to	Related words
comparisons (cont.)	hyper- hypo- intra- iso- macro- med- meta- micro- para- peri- post- pre- proto- re- retro- sub- super-, supra- ultra-	excessive, over inadequate, beneath within equal, balanced relatively large between, in the middle next to, beyond relatively small similar to, resembling surrounding, outside of after, following before, preceding early, first again behind below above, greater than to an extreme, beyond	hypertension, hypersecretion hypochondriac, hyposecretion intramuscular isotonic macrophage median, mediastinal metacarpals microscopic parathyroid, parasympathetic pericardium, peritoneum, perineum posthepatic jaundice, posterior premature birth, premolar protoplasm respiratory retroperitoneal subcutaneous, sublingual superior, superficial, suprarenal gland ultrasound, ultraviolet
numbers, amounts	uni- mono- bi- tri- quad- poly-	one one two three four many	unit, unicellular, universal donor monocyte, monosaccharide biceps, bicuspid triceps, tricuspid quadrant polypeptide, polyuria
general	acute appendicular axial corpus foramen fossa meatus plane, planus plexus pneumo terminal torso	sharp, coming quickly attached to the main part of a structure (from Latin for *body*) a hole (from Latin for a *bored hole*) a pit, depression (from Latin for *ditch*) a natural body opening (from Latin for *passageway*) a flat surface (from Latin for *flat*) a point of interwoven structures (from Latin for *braid*) relating to the respiratory system (from Latin for *air*) relating to an end point the main portion of the body from the shoulders to the hips	acute pain, acute illness appendicular skeleton axial skeleton corpus luteum, corpuscle foramen magnum, foramen ovale mandibular fossa external auditory meatus frontal plane, sagittal plane sacral plexus, brachial plexus pneumonia, pneumothorax terminal illness torso
plurals	-a -um -us	becomes -ae becomes -a becomes -i	fossa/fossae, vena/venae atrium/atria, bacterium/bacteria bacillus/bacilli

Student Supplement 2—Anatomical Terms

INTRODUCTION

As you have learned, health-care professionals must become familiar with a special vocabulary. Many of these words are based on Greek, Latin, or other foreign languages. Student Supplement 1 covers a number of these terms, especially those that will help you to understand the location and function of body parts. Additionally, there are specific terms for given areas of the body. This student supplement presents the most-common medical terms for body regions and parts. Because muscles, nerves, bones, blood vessels, and other structures often take their names from their location, knowing these words will help you to more easily learn anatomy and related terms.

Table 1
Anatomical Terms

Term	Related part	Term	Related part
abdominal (ab-dawm´-uhn-uhl)	lower anterior torso	mandibular (man-dib´-yuh-luhr)	jaw
acromial (ak-ro´-me-uhl)	shoulder	mental (ment´-uhl)	chin
antebrachial (ant-e-bra´-ke-uhl)	forearm	nasal (na´-zuhl)	nose
axillary (ak´-suh-ler-e)	armpit	occipital (awk-sip´-uht-uhl)	back of the head
brachial (bra´-ke-uhl)	upper arm	olecranal (o-lek´-ran-uhl)	back of the elbow
buccal (buhk´-uhl)	mouth or cheeks	oral (or´-uhl)	mouth
calcaneal (kal-ka´-ne-uhl)	heel of the foot	orbital (or´-buht-uhl)	eye
cardiac (kard´-e-ak)	heart	otic (awt´-ik)	ear
carpal (kar´-puhl)	wrist	palmar (pal´-muhr)	palm
cephalic (suh-fal´-ik)	head	parietal (puh-ri´-uht-uhl)	crown of the head
cervical (suhr´-vi-kuhl)	neck	patellar (puh-tel´-uhr)	kneecap
coxal (kawk´-suhl)	hip	pectoral (pek´-truhl)	chest
cranial (kra´-ne-uhl)	head	pedal (ped´-uhl)	foot
crural (krur´-uhl)	leg	pelvic (pel´-vik)	area defined by hips
cubital (kyu´-buht-uhl)	elbow	perineal (per-uh-ne´-uhl)	pelvic floor
cutaneous (kyu-ta´-ne-uhs)	skin	plantar (plant´-uhr)	sole of a foot
deltoid (del´-toid)	shoulder	pollex (pawl´-eks)	thumb
dental (dent´-uhl)	the teeth	popliteal (pawp-luh-te´-uhl)	back of a knee
digital (dij´-uht-uhl)	finger or toe	pubic (pyu´-bik)	anterior region of groin
dorsal (dor´-suhl)	upper back		
femoral (fem´-uhruhl)	thigh	pulmonary (pul´-muh-ner-e)	lungs
frontal (fruhnt´-uhl)	forehead	renal (ren´-uhl)	kidneys
gastric (gas´-trik)	stomach	sacral (sak´-ruhl)	base of the spine
gluteal (glut´-e-uhl)	buttocks	sural (sur´-uhl)	calf
hepatic (hi-pat´-ik)	liver	tarsal (tar´-suhl)	ankle
iliac (il´-e-ak)	hip	temporal (tem´-puhruhl)	side of the head
inguinal (in´-gwuhn-uhl)	groin	thoracic (thuh-ras´-ik)	chest
lingual (ling´-gwuhl)	tongue	umbilical (uhm-bil´-i-kuhl)	navel
lumbar (luhm´-buhr)	small of the back	volar (vo´-luhr)	palm
mammary (mam´-uh-re)	breast		

SECTION A:
Introduction to Anatomy and Physiology

Module 2-A: Biochemistry and Microbiology

Module Contents

Assignment Sheets

1— Construct a Model of a Typical Cell

2— Develop a Presentation on Bacteria, Viruses, Fungi, or Parasites

3— Practice Critical Thinking: Complete Biochemistry and Microbiology Case Studies

PREREQUISITE:
Module 1-A

Learning Activities Sheet

Student name _____

DIRECTIONS

Place a checkmark in the appropriate box as you complete each of the steps below.

❑ 1. **Take**   Pretest provided by your instructor.

❑ 2. **Stop**   Have your instructor evaluate your performance. Follow your instructor's recommendations concerning the following learning activities.

❑ 3. **Read**   Module Objective Sheet.

❑ 4. **Study**   Information Sheet, Objectives 1 through 40.

❑ 5. **Research** Online resources to learn more about biochemistry and microbiology. Your instructor will list several Web sites on the blanks below. Visit at least three of the following Internet sites.

• _____

• _____

• _____

• _____

• _____

• _____

• _____

❑ 6. **Do**   Assignment Sheet 1, "Construct a Model of a Typical Cell."

❑ 7. **Stop**   Have your instructor evaluate your performance. If the evaluation is satisfactory, continue to step 8. If the evaluation is not satisfactory, repeat step 6.

❑ 8. **Study**   Information Sheet, Objectives 41 through 52.

❑ 9. **Do**   Assignment Sheet 2, "Develop a Presentation on Bacteria, Viruses, Fungi, or Parasites."

❑ 10. **Stop**   Have your instructor evaluate your performance. If the evaluation is satisfactory, continue to step 11. If the evaluation is not satisfactory, repeat step 9.

❏ 11. **Do**   Assignment Sheet 3, "Practice Critical Thinking: Complete Biochemistry and Microbiology Case Studies."

❏ 12. **Stop**   Have your instructor evaluate your performance. If the evaluation is satisfactory, continue to step 13. If the evaluation is not satisfactory, repeat step 11.

❏ 13. **Take**   Written Test provided by your instructor.

❏ 14. **Stop**   Have your instructor evaluate your performance. If the evaluation is satisfactory, continue to step 15. If the evaluation is not satisfactory, repeat steps 4 and 8.

❏ 15. **Check**   With your instructor for any additional assignments to be completed.

❏ 16. **Do**   Additional assignments your instructor lists below.

_____

_____

_____

❏ 17. **Take**   Module Review provided by your instructor.

❏ 18. **Stop**   Have your instructor evaluate your performance. Follow your instructor's recommendations concerning a review of the above learning activities.

❏ 19. **Stop**   Have your instructor evaluate your performance on this module by compiling your scores on the Written Test, assignment sheets, and Module Review. If the evaluation is satisfactory, proceed to the next module. If the evaluation is not satisfactory, ask your instructor for further instructions.

*Permission to duplicate this Learning Activities Sheet is granted.

Module Objective Sheet

MODULE OBJECTIVE

After completing this module, you should be able to describe the role of the major elements and compounds found in the human body, discuss the factors that affect cell growth and reproduction, and describe the classes of microorganisms found in the human body. You should demonstrate these competencies by completing the assignment sheets and by scoring a minimum of 85 percent on the Written Test and on the Module Review.

SPECIFIC OBJECTIVES

After completing this module, you should be able to:

1.   Define the terms *biochemistry* and *microbiology.*

2.   Discuss the role of chemistry in human health.

3.   Define the term *homeostasis.*

4.   Define the term *element.*

5.   Define the term *atom.*

6.   Label the parts of an atom.

7.   Define the term *molecule.*

8.   Distinguish among the terms *compound, mixture,* and *solution.*

9.   Describe the primary role of each of the principal elements and compounds in the body.

10.   Complete statements that describe the chemical reactions that take place in the body.

11.   State the functions of the major types of organic compounds in the body.

12.   Match components of the major types of organic compounds in the body to their characteristics.

13.   Complete statements that describe the major elements and compounds that compose the body.

14.   Define types of solutions.

15.   Define the major types of fluid in the body.

16.   Define the term *electrolyte.*

17.   Discuss the role of electrolytes in human health.

18. Select true statements concerning the role of acids and bases in human health.

19. Define the term *metabolism*.

20. Complete statements that describe the use of energy by the body.

21. Complete statements that describe the characteristics of body temperature.

22. State definitions of the basic activities that define life.

23. State the cell theory.

24. Match the compounds found in protoplasm to their functions.

25. Define the principal types of protoplasm.

26. Label the major parts of a cell.

27. Match the major parts of a cell to their functions.

28. Describe the major parts of a cell nucleus.

29. Describe the specialized structures in cells.

30. State the functions of the specialized structures in cells.

31. List the functions of a cell.

32. Define the term *transport*.

33. Distinguish between the terms *active transport* and *passive transport*.

34. Match types of passive transport to their descriptions.

35. Match types of active transport to their descriptions.

36. Complete statements that describe the process of cell growth.

37. Distinguish between the types of cell reproduction.

38. Describe the process in which the genetic makeup of a cell can be changed.

39. List the sources of mutation-causing conditions.

40. Match the types of cellular respiration to their descriptions.

41. Arrange in order the levels in the taxonomy system used to classify organisms.

42. Match the types of relationships between organisms to their descriptions.

43. Match classes of microorganisms to their descriptions.

44. Label the classes of microorganisms as classified by their shape.

45. Define the terms *resident flora* and *transient flora.*

46. Describe the purpose of a gram stain.

47. Complete statements that describe the characteristics of bacteria.

48. Complete statements that describe the characteristics of rickettsiae.

49. Complete statements that describe the characteristics of viruses.

50. Complete statements that describe the characteristics of protozoa.

51. Distinguish between fungi and algae.

52. Complete statements that describe common parasites that afflict humans.

53. Construct a model of a typical cell. (Assignment Sheet 1)

54. Develop a presentation on bacteria, viruses, fungi, or parasites. (Assignment Sheet 2)

55. Practice critical thinking: complete biochemistry and microbiology case studies. (Assignment Sheet 3)

Information Sheet

OBJECTIVE 1

The terms *biochemistry and microbiology*

KEY TERMS

Energy (en´-uhr-je)—The capacity to do work

✔ **Note:** The definition presented here is the classic scientific definition of the term *energy.* Work can be understood as a force that can bring about change in matter or other types of energy. That force may change the shape or the state of the matter, such as bending a bar or melting ice. Energy is classed as kinetic (energy in motion) or potential (stored energy). There are also several forms of energy, including light, sound, heat, mechanical, chemical, electrical, and radiation. All of these forms are involved in the functioning of the body and its care through medical practices. For example, there is stored chemical energy in the food we eat. The body converts that stored energy into heat energy, which can help the functioning of the body.

Matter (mat´-uhr)—That portion of the universe that has shape and substance

---

a. Biochemistry—The study of chemistry as it relates to life

✔ **Note:** Everything in the universe exists as either **matter** or **energy**. Another name for matter is *chemicals,* and the study of what matter is made of is called *chemistry.* The study of chemistry as it relates to life is referred to as *biological chemistry* or simply *biochemistry.* The two basic functions of chemicals in the body are to provide structure to the body and to provide a source of energy to support life.

b. Microbiology—The study of extremely small life

✔ **Note:** *Bio-* is a prefix that means *life,* and *biology* is the study of life. Another prefix is *micro-,* which means *extremely small.* Thus, *microbiology* is the study of extremely small life. In this module, you will study the chemical nature of life and will consider the smallest building blocks of life—from chemicals to the cells that those chemicals form and support.

Module 2-A: Biochemistry and Microbiology

OBJECTIVE 2	**Role of chemistry in human health**

KEY TERMS

Chemical reaction (kem´-i-kuhl re-ak´-shuhn)—A process in which one or more chemicals that are exposed to other chemicals or sources of energy such as heat change their chemical composition to produce other chemicals and often other forms of energy

Gas (gas´)—A state of matter in which the substance will take on the shape of any container in which it is placed and will expand to fill the container

Liquid (lik´-wuhd)—A state of matter in which the substance will take on the shape of a container but will not expand to fill a container with greater volume than the substance

Nutrient (nu´-tre-uhnt)—A substance that can be processed by the digestive system and used by the cells to produce energy or build tissue

Respiration (res-puh-ra´-shuhn)—The physical and chemical processes by which an organism supplies its cells and tissues with oxygen and removes carbon dioxide

Solid (sawl´-uhd)—A state of matter in which the substance has a definite shape that is maintained unless acted upon by a force that is capable of changing that shape

---

a. The body consists of various chemicals.

   ✔ **Note:** The major chemicals of the body are oxygen (65 percent), carbon (19 percent), hydrogen (10 percent), and nitrogen (3 percent). Water, which makes up almost three-fourths of a person's body weight, consists of oxygen and hydrogen. Matter exists in three primary forms: **liquids**, **gases**, and **solids**. Chemicals are found in the body in all three forms. Bones and muscle are primarily solids. Blood and saliva are liquids. The air in the lungs and throughout the cavities in the body consists of gases.

b. Most body activities involve **chemical reactions**.

   ✔ **Note:** The basic chemical reaction in the body is referred to as *cell respiration*. In cell respiration, the chemical glucose, a sugar found in many foods, combines with oxygen that has been breathed into the lungs and carried to the cells by the blood system. The reaction between these two chemicals produces the chemicals carbon dioxide, water, and adenosine triphosphate (ATP), as well as heat. Carbon dioxide is carried in the bloodstream to the lungs and breathed out, while the water is used in various ways, including to help maintain the structure and chemical balance of the cells. ATP provides energy for other chemical reactions within the cell. The heat helps to warm the body and improves the efficiency of some chemical reactions.

c. For a person to remain healthy, the chemicals within the body must remain properly balanced.

✔ **Note:** Chemical imbalances can occur for a number of reasons related to the chemicals we take into the body or how those chemicals are processed internally. We obtain vitamins and minerals from the foods we eat. If a person's diet does not contain sufficient amounts of these vitamins and minerals, his or her health can be affected. For example, a person may not get enough iron in the diet. Iron is essential to healthy blood, and iron deficiency can lead to a condition in which the blood is not able to carry oxygen and **nutrients** effectively. On the other hand, a person who has sufficient iron intake may suffer the same condition if the iron cannot be digested and absorbed through the walls of the stomach and intestines.

d. The body also produces special chemicals that regulate body functions.

✔ **Note:** The organs and glands of the body produce various chemicals used to carry out body functions. Some specialized chemicals called *hormones* have specific roles in controlling growth, reproduction, and overall health. In some instances, the body may produce too much of a chemical, such as excessive digestive-fluid production, which can lead to holes called *ulcers* in the digestive tract.

e. Chemicals entering the body from the external environment can affect the balance of chemicals within the body and can disrupt normal physiological chemical reactions.

✔ **Note:** Chemicals enter the body through the nose, mouth, and other openings; through breaks in the skin; and through the skin itself. In some cases, it is important to have chemicals enter the body, such as when oxygen enters the body during breathing. However, a person may also breathe in harmful chemicals. The harm that such chemicals cause is generally the result of disrupting normal functions. For example, a person may inhale carbon monoxide if sitting in a parked car while it is running. Carbon monoxide readily attaches to the red blood cells that normally carry oxygen throughout the body. If the red blood cells are loaded with carbon monoxide, they cannot accept oxygen as they pass through the lungs. If enough carbon monoxide enters the bloodstream so that there is not adequate oxygen getting to the brain and other vital organs, eventually the person affected will lose consciousness and even die if not removed from the source of the carbon monoxide. Another way in which a person can be adversely affected by chemicals occurs when organisms such as harmful viruses enter the body. These organisms may produce chemicals called *toxins* that disrupt body functions.

f. Injuries and diseases can change the chemical balance within the body and can disrupt chemical reactions.

✔ **Note:** Injuries and diseases can affect the body's abilities to produce chemicals internally or to process chemicals taken in from external sources. For example, diabetes is a family of conditions that affect the body's ability to convert glucose to energy and other chemicals.

OBJECTIVE 3	**The term *homeostasis***

Homeostasis (ho-me-o-sta'-suhs)—The state of the body in which conditions remain relatively stable despite changes in the environment

✔ **Note:** Basically, the human body is a chemical engine. Humans place chemicals (food) in the body and subject those substances to chemicals within the body to create chemical reactions. One's health depends on providing the body with the proper amounts and types of chemical and the body's ability to properly process those chemicals. One aspect of chemical processing within the body is responding to changes in the environment in order to maintain health. For example, the human body functions best at a temperature between approximately 97°F and 99°F (36°C and 38°C). If the temperature of the outside environment drops, the body will increase its production of energy and reduce blood circulation in the extremities to ensure adequate warmth for the vital organs. On a hot day, the body will sweat more, which removes heat from the body and increases cooling of the skin due to the evaporation of the perspiration. These and other reactions to changes in the external and internal environment of the body help to maintain homeostasis.

OBJECTIVE 4	**The term *element***

Element—One of more than 100 primary, simple substances that cannot be broken down by chemical means into any other substance

OBJECTIVE 5	**The term *atom***

KEY TERM

Atomic (uh-tawm'-ik) **number**—The number of protons, or positive charges, in the nucleus of an atom of a particular element

---

Atom—The smallest division of an element that exhibits all the properties and characteristics of the element

✔ **Note:** All matter is made up of three smaller particles: neutrons, electrons, and protons (see Objective 6). The number of protons in the nucleus of an atom determines the **atomic number** of the element.

| OBJECTIVE 6 | **Parts of an atom** |

> KEY TERM
>
> **Bond** (bawnd´)—The mechanism by which atoms link to one another to form molecules involving the loss of, gaining of, or sharing of electrons in the outer shell
>
> ✔ **Note:** There are three types of chemical bonds among atoms. In an *ionic bond*, an atom gives up one or more electrons to another atom. This results in the atom having more protons than electrons, giving it a positive charge. The atom that gains electrons has more electrons than protons, meaning that the atom has a negative charge. The difference in charges holds the atoms together. In what is called *covalent bonding*, an atom that does not have an outer shell that is filled to its full capacity with electrons can share electrons with one or more other atoms. Finally, hydrogen is the smallest atom with only one proton and one electron. When hydrogen shares its electron with another atom, it causes a slightly positive charge in the atom, making it particularly attractive to oxygen and nitrogen atoms, which are slightly negative. This special attraction is referred to as *hydrogen bonding*. Hydrogen bonds are especially important in the human body because hydrogen bonds help hold water molecules together, as well as many of the proteins that are essential to body structure and functioning.

✔ **Note:** All matter is made of particles called *atoms.* Atoms, in turn, consist of three smaller particles (see Figure 1). In the center of the atom, termed the *nucleus*, are *protons* and *neutrons*. The third particle is called an *electron.* Electrons go around the nucleus in orbits, with each electron following a separate path. The atoms of different materials differ in the number of each type of particle they contain. Generally, there is an equal number of electrons, protons, and neutrons in an atom. For example, a hydrogen atom contains one of each of the particles, while an oxygen atom consists of eight electrons, protons, and neutrons each. As the number of electrons increases, the additional groups of orbits that are required are found at greater distances from the nucleus. All the orbits that are at an equal distance from the nucleus are referred to as a *shell.* Each shell is capable of supporting a specific number of electrons. The electrons in the outer shell can be shared with other atoms to form **bonds**. Atoms that bond to each other form structures called *molecules* (see Objective 7).

a. Electron (i-lek´-trawn)—A negatively charged elementary particle of an atom

b. Neutron (nu´-trawn)—An elementary particle that is a fundamental component of the nucleus of atoms; it has no electric charge

c. Nucleus (nu´-kle-uhs)—The structure in the center of an atom consisting of protons and neutrons and about which electrons orbit

> ✔ **Note:** The nucleus of each element is unique to that substance. Hydrogen is the smallest atom, with one neutron and one proton in its nucleus. Helium has two neutrons and two protons. This progression continues through the natural elements up to uranium with 92 neutrons and protons. The number of protons and neutrons is used to identify each element and is called its *atomic number.* Two of the more-common elements in the body, along with hydrogen, are carbon, with an atomic number of 6, and oxygen, with an atomic number of 8.

d. Proton (pro´-tawn)—A positively charged particle that is a fundamental component of the nucleus of atoms

e. Shell (shel´)—The set of electron orbits in an atom that have the same energy level

✔ **Note:** The innermost shell of atoms can hold up to two electrons. Thus, hydrogen and helium have one shell. The second shell or energy level consists of electrons with orbits that are farther from the nucleus than the innermost shell. The second shell can have as many as eight electrons, which means that the elements up to atomic number 10 (neon) have only two shells. Additional shells hold eight electrons or up to a multiple of eight electrons.

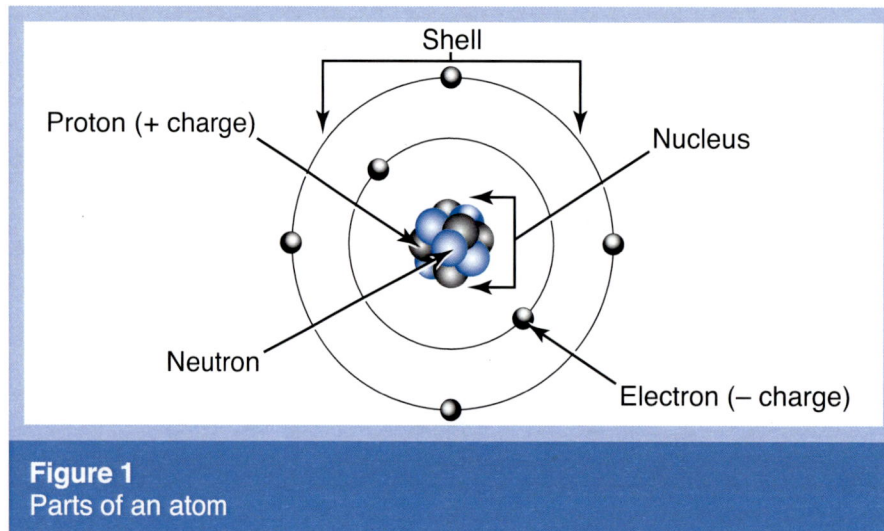

Figure 1
Parts of an atom

OBJECTIVE 7

The term *molecule*

Molecule—A structure consisting of two or more atoms

✔ **Note:** A molecule may consist of atoms of the same element or atoms of two or more different elements. For example, oxygen in the air is often present as molecules of two atoms, which is written using the symbol for oxygen (O) and a subscript 2 to show that there are two atoms: O_2. Water is a compound, and its molecules consist of two hydrogen (H) atoms and one oxygen atom, represented symbolically as H_2O.

| OBJECTIVE 8 | **The terms *compound, mixture,* and *solution*** |

KEY TERMS

Catalyst (kat´-uhl-uhst)—A substance that affects the rate of change in a chemical reaction without being changed chemically

✔ **Note:** Generally, a catalyst will cause a reaction to begin or will cause the reaction to proceed at a faster rate. However, the catalyst itself is not affected by the reaction. As stated in the previous note, energy can have a catalytic effect, such as stirring sugar into a solution or heating the solution to increase the amount of sugar that will dissolve. Time, pressure, light, and other factors may also affect the efficiency of a chemical reaction.

Centrifuge (sen´-truh-fyuj)—A device that is used to separate the components of a solution or liquid mixture by spinning the substance

✔ **Note:** One of the laws of physics deals with centrifugal force. Basically, this law is a variation on the law of inertia, which states, in part, that an object in motion tends to continue in motion in a straight line unless acted upon by another force. When an object is spun in a circle, it tries to move in a straight line, but it is forced to follow a curved path. If the object is spinning fast enough, any substance that is free to move within the object will move toward the outside of the circular path. This explains why water will remain in a bucket if you swing the bucket over your head. The heavier the freely moving substance is, the quicker it will move toward the outside of the circular path. This principle can be used in medicine to separate the substances in a liquid, such as the cells in blood. A centrifuge is used to accomplish this separation.

Concentration (kawn-sen-tra´-shuhn)—The ratio of the components of a solution or mixture

✔ **Note:** Assume that a certain medication is to be mixed with an equal amount of water before being provided to the patient, using 0.5 liter of medicine and 0.5 liter of water. The resulting solution would be half water and half medicine. It could then be referred to as a 50 percent solution of medicine (or water). Solutions are often referred to as *percentages*. Thus, a 1 percent saline solution would be 99 percent water and 1 percent salt. Generally, these percentages refer to the volume of the substances in solution though occasionally measurements are made as weight. Also, concentrations are sometimes given as ratios rather than as percentages. The 50 percent solution of medicine described earlier can also be referred to as a 1:1 ratio, meaning that for one measure of medicine there is one measure of water.

Saturation point (sach-uh-ra´-shuhn point´)—The concentration level of a solution above which no more of a substance will dissolve

✔ **Note:** If one continues to add a *solute*—the substance being dissolved—to a liquid, at some point there will be more solute than the liquid can dissolve. This is called the *saturation point*. The saturation point can be changed through the use of catalysts, heat, stirring, and in other ways. One can also add more *solvent*—the liquid—but this does not actually change the saturation point if all other conditions remain the same. It simply lowers the concentration of solute, allowing more to be added if desired.

✔ **Note:** When substances are put together, they form relationships that may or may not involve a chemical reaction between them. A chemical reaction (see Objective 10) results in a change in the reacting chemicals. For example, in a reaction between two compounds, the atoms may be rearranged to form one or more other compounds or they may simply break into the elements that make up the original compounds. In other instances, nothing chemical happens between substances that are mixed together. Whether a reaction takes place depends on a number of factors—most importantly, the chemicals involved and the presence or absence of **catalysts**.

a. Compound—A substance that consists of atoms of two or more different elements bonded together as molecules; to separate its components into other compounds and elements requires a chemical reaction

b. Mixture—A substance that consists of two or more combined components that do not interact chemically; to separate its components requires either a mechanical method or the application of energy

   ✔ **Note:** Numerous methods exist for separating mixtures, many of which are applied to medical procedures. One method of separating mixtures in which the substances are different sizes is filtration in which the mixture is forced through a material that allows smaller substances to pass through while preventing the passage of larger particles. Blood, urine, and other body fluids are sometimes filtered to remove impurities or certain components. In some cases, energy is used to separate the substances. For example, a mixture may be spun in a **centrifuge** to separate substances based on their mass (weight). An electrical charge can be used to remove negative or positive ions.

c. Solution—A substance that consists of one or more components dissolved in a liquid; to separate its components, the energy of the substance must change so that the energy balance between the components prevents the liquid from being able to hold the dissolved material

   ✔ **Note:** Whether a substance will dissolve in a liquid depends on a number of factors. Consider placing sugar in water. If one places a teaspoon of sugar in a glass of water, some of the sugar will dissolve and some will settle to the bottom. The chemical relationship between water and sugar allows the sugar to dissolve, but at a relatively slow rate. If the solution is stirred, more of the sugar will dissolve because the stirring adds mechanical energy to the solution. Similarly, if the solution is heated, more sugar will dissolve because of the heat energy. However, if one keeps increasing the **concentration** of sugar, eventually the solution will reach its **saturation point** and no more sugar will dissolve even with additional stirring or heat.

| OBJECTIVE 9 | **Primary role of each of the principal elements and compounds in the body** |

KEY TERMS

Exhalation (eks-huh-la´-shuhn) — The act of breathing out or exhaling

✔ **Note:** Breathing consists of two steps. Taking air into the lungs is called *inhalation* or *inspiration*. Breathing out is called *exhalation* or *expiration*.

Lubricate (lu´-bruh-kat) — To improve the ease of movement between two objects by applying a substance that reduces friction

✔ **Note:** Friction is the resistance to movement of objects that are in contact with each other. For example, if you press your hands against each other and try to move them, it takes some effort. If you cover your hands with soap and water and rub them against each other it takes less effort because the soap and water have reduced the friction. You may also notice that when you rub your dry hands together, they get warm. This is a result of friction. While you cannot see it, you also rub cells and parts of dead tissue off your hands. Inside the body, where structures rub against each other, such as at the joints between bones, there is friction. Water and fluids largely composed of water in the body help reduce that friction, which allows the body structures to last longer.

Organic compound (or-gan´-ik kawm-paund´) — A compound that contains carbon and hydrogen

✔ **Note:** Life on earth is referred to as being *carbon-based* because the physical structures of all organisms are made principally of compounds that contain carbon and hydrogen. Compounds that do not contain carbon and hydrogen, such as water, are referred to as *inorganic compounds.*

a. Oxygen (awk´-si-juhn) — Required for the chemical reaction that releases energy from nutrients; one of the atoms in a water molecule; a key element in other compounds of importance to the body

   ✔ **Note:** The earth's atmosphere is approximately 21 percent oxygen, which we take into the body by breathing and, to a much lesser degree, through the breakdown of oxygen-containing compounds in nutrients. Oxygen is required for the release of energy within the cells. Oxygen is also an important part of water (H_2O). The body is approximately 60 to 75 percent water. Much of the rest of the body is composed of **organic compounds**, which often contain oxygen in their structure.

b. Carbon dioxide (kar´-buhn di-awk´-sid) — Given off as a waste product of cell respiration

   ✔ **Note:** Carbon dioxide is a compound consisting of molecules with one carbon atom and two oxygen atoms (CO_2). When nutrients are converted to energy, excess atoms of carbon and oxygen combine to form carbon dioxide. Carbon dioxide is carried to the lungs, from which it is returned to the atmosphere through **exhalation**. If the body is unable to remove CO_2 at a sufficient rate so that the gas builds up in the body, acids form and may lead to a condition called *acidosis*, which can interfere with normal functioning of the body. Diseases such as pneumonia may impair normal elimination of carbon dioxide.

c.   Water (wawt´-uhr)—Dissolves substances to make them more usable to the body; provides fluid to **lubricate** moving parts of the body; helps to maintain body temperature

✔ **Note:** The process of moving nutrients and chemicals through the body is highly dependent on water because most of these substances must be dissolved in order to pass through the body and into cells. Water is an effective solvent and dissolves directly or indirectly (as the liquid part of blood, for example) most of the chemicals that must be transported through the body. The process actually begins with saliva in the mouth. This water begins dissolving nutrients. It also lubricates the food to make it easier to chew and to swallow. In the digestive tract, water helps to carry nutrient chemicals through membranes and to the cells. Finally, water heats and cools slowly. Because most of the volume of the body is saturated with water, body temperature does not change quickly with changes in environmental temperature, helping to maintain homeostasis.

d.   Glucose (glu´-kos)—Serves as the primary energy source for the cells

✔ **Note:** Glucose is a complex compound that consists of 6 carbon atoms, 12 hydrogen atoms, and 6 oxygen atoms ($C_6H_{12}O_6$). It belongs to a class of chemicals called *monosaccharides* (mawn-uh-sak´-uh-rids) or *simple sugars.* Glucose may be taken into the body in nutrients, or it may be produced by the liver from other sugars.

OBJECTIVE 10

Chemical reactions that take place in the body

KEY TERMS

Fever (fe´-vuhr)—An abnormally high body temperature

✔ **Note:** Fever often accompanies a number of diseases. Body temperature is discussed in more detail in Objective 21.

Theory (the´-uh-re)—A statement that provides an explanation based on evidence without final proof being obtained

✔ **Note:** Like the active site theory, there are many ideas about how the body functions that cannot be proved. Many of these will probably be proved or disproved as science continues to make advances, such as new methods for examining processes inside the body. The explanations offered by theories are not guesses. Theories are based on known facts and attempt to take those facts into consideration in their explanations.

---

a.   A chemical reaction involves an interaction between two or more chemicals that results in matter with a different chemical composition from the chemicals that were originally introduced into the reaction.

✔ **Note:** Chemists record chemical reactions with symbols similar to math equations. For example, the basic reaction in the cells that converts glucose into energy can be written:

$$C_6H_{12}O_6 + 6O_2 \rightarrow 6CO_2 + 6H_2O + heat$$

This formula shows that when a molecule of glucose ($C_6H_{12}O_6$) is combined with 6 molecules of oxygen (O_2) it is converted into (➜) 6 molecules of carbon dioxide (CO_2), 6 molecules of water (H_2O), and heat. The glucose comes from digested food, while the oxygen is taken into the lungs during respiration. Both glucose and oxygen are delivered to the cells by the circulatory system. The carbon dioxide is returned to the bloodstream and breathed out from the lungs. The water is used to maintain the health of the cells and to transport substances in and out of the cells, while the heat produced is the energy that allows the cells to do work. Note that there are 6 carbon atoms, 12 hydrogen, and 18 oxygen atoms on each side of the equation.

b. A reaction that causes atoms or molecules to bond, thus producing different chemicals, is called a *synthesis reaction*.

✔ **Note:** An example of a synthesis reaction would be the formation of water:

$$2H_2 + O_2 ➜ 2H_2O$$

In this formula, free hydrogen and free oxygen molecules bind through hydrogen bonds to form or *synthesize* water.

c. A reaction that causes molecule bonds to break is called a *decomposition reaction*.

✔ **Note:** The conversion of glucose and oxygen into carbon dioxide, water, and heat is a decomposition reaction. While it is true that new compounds are formed, the reaction begins by decomposing existing molecules by breaking their bonds.

d. Synthesis reactions are necessary to allow the body to build proteins and other building blocks of cells and tissue.

e. Decomposition reactions are necessary to allow the body to break down the large, complex molecules of nutrients into small, easily transported molecules that the cells can use to sustain life.

✔ **Note:** While it is true that there are proteins in the foods we eat, most of them are not directly usable by the body. Most proteins are broken into their carbon, hydrogen, oxygen, and nitrogen components so that the body can build the proteins that it needs, such as hemoglobin and collagen.

f. Catalysts or energy can be added to a chemical reaction to increase the rate of reaction.

✔ **Note:** Enzymes are perhaps the most-important catalysts in the body because they are responsible for assisting in thousands of kinds of reactions. According to the active site theory, enzymes perform their catalytic function because of their shapes. Each enzyme has receptor sites on the outer surfaces. The chemical that a particular enzyme catalyzes has a shape that exactly fits the enzyme's receptor site, much like the pieces of a jigsaw puzzle fit together. Each enzyme receptor site exactly matches one chemical molecule, referred to as a *substrate*. For example, the digestive enzyme involved in the breakdown of the muscle protein of ingested meat will not catalyze the starch in potatoes. Generally, the enzyme can be envisioned to attach to a chemical and pull it away from a molecule. Another receptor site then attaches to a second chemical and pulls it from its molecule. The chemicals in the receptor sites then form bonds with each other and release from the enzyme. Thus, a new substance is produced and the enzyme is left unchanged.

g. The failure to provide the reactive chemicals in the proper proportions, the introduction of additional chemicals, or the failure to provide a required catalyst or energy source can prevent the reaction from happening.

✔ **Note:** A poor diet can lead to not having the proper chemicals in the body, and disease may interfere with normal chemical reactions. For example, with certain illnesses, the body may develop acidosis, or an excess of acid, and the accompanying positive hydrogen ions (H+). In some instances, these hydrogen ions may attach to enzyme receptor sites that would normally break down carbohydrates and other chemicals or the ions may change the shape of the enzyme, making it impossible for the enzyme to perform its function. The **fever** that accompanies some illnesses may increase the temperature to a point that the internal bonds of the enzyme break down and are unable to perform their function. Enzymes that have changed shapes are said to be *denatured.*

OBJECTIVE 11

Functions of the major types of organic compounds in the body

---

KEY TERM

Genetic code (juh-net´-ik kod´)—The sequence of bases in DNA that determines how the organism will be structured

✔ **Note:** The segments of DNA called *genes* each have a specific purpose in determining the characteristics of the organism. Some traits are common to a given type of organism. For example, genes for the number of fingers and toes, eyes, and ears, and their locations are pretty much the same from person to person. However, the gene sequence that determines the color of the eyes and the shape of the ears will vary from person to person. Genetic code is especially important to health professionals because the code helps to determine whether a particular person is likely to become afflicted with certain illnesses or conditions. For example, a person may be more likely to have high blood pressure, liver cancer, or a heart condition because of that person's genetic code.

---

a. Carbohydrates (kar-bo-hi´-drats)—Serve as the major source of energy

b. Lipids (lip´-uhds)—Serve as a means of storing energy, providing structure to cell membranes, and influencing some hormone functions

c. Proteins (pro´-tens)—Serve many roles in the human body that can be generally classed as *functional,* in which the protein regulates a chemical reaction, or *structural,* in which the protein is a component in cells and tissues

✔ **Note:** All proteins are large molecules called *macromolecules* and are the most-abundant organic chemical in the body.

d. Nucleic (nu-kle´-ik) acids—Serve to encode and decode information required for the production of structural protein

✔ **Note:** The nucleic acids provide a coded plan for how an individual organism is supposed to be assembled. This coded plan is referred to as the *genetic code.*

OBJECTIVE 12	Components of the major types of organic compounds in the body

KEY TERMS

Antibody (ant´-i-bawd-e)—A protein molecule that will bind to foreign substances in the body

✔ **Note:** Antibodies are part of the immune system that protects the body against invasion by foreign organisms. Every cell—those in the body and those that may enter the body from outside—have markers, proteins called *antigens* in their cell walls. The body recognizes the antigens of its own cells, but when a foreign antigen is encountered, the body produces antibodies that can attach to the foreign antigen. The antibodies are produced by plasma cells in the blood. The receptor sites on the antibody are specific to the foreign antigen.

Enzyme (en´-zim)—A protein that acts as a catalyst in a chemical reaction

✔ **Note:** Enzymes are sometimes referred to as *organic catalysts*. Enzymes are located throughout the body. For example, the saliva, gastric juices, and secretions of the intestine contain enzymes to help digest food.

Inflammatory response (in-flam´-uh-tor-e ri-spawns´)—The way the body reacts to an injury

✔ **Note:** The inflammatory response may include redness, swelling, and heat due to increased blood flow and pain due to the chemicals released by injured and dying cells. The response is ordered and normal.

Pore (por´)—An opening in a surface that allows materials to pass through

✔ **Note:** Pores are found in the skin, in organs, and in the cells themselves to allow the flow of materials that support life. For example, pores in the skin allow the release of perspiration, body oils, and other secretions that help to maintain homeostasis and health. Pores at the cellular level allow nutrients to penetrate the cell and allow the elimination of wastes.

Sexual maturation (sek´-shuhl mach-uh-ra´-shuhn)—The process of developing secondary sexual characteristics and becoming able to reproduce

a. Carbohydrates

- Consist primarily of sugars or saccharides (sak´-uh-rids)

- Include monosaccharides (mawn-uh-sak´-uh-rids), which are simple sugars that provide nutrient energy and form other compounds

   ✔ **Note:** Simple sugars contain five carbon atoms and are called *pentose* or contain six carbon atoms and are referred to as *hexose*. There are three principal hexose saccharides that are important to the body: glucose (glu´-kos), fructose (fruhk´-tos), and galactose (guh-lak´-tos). Glucose is the major source of energy. The liver can convert fructose and galactose into glucose when extra energy is needed.

- Include ribose (ri´-bos) and deoxyribose (de-awk´-si-ri-bos), which are part of the nucleic acids that form the genetic code in cells

  ✔ **Note:** The two most-important pentose monosaccharides are ribose and deoxyribose. Their primary importance is in the formation of nucleic acids—proteins that carry the chemical "blueprint" of how the body is to be formed and the code for traits such as hair color, handedness, eye color, etc.

- Include oligosaccharides (awl-i-go-sak´-uh-rids), which serve as antigens on the outer surface of cell membranes

  ✔ **Note:** There are other sugars that are more complex than mono-saccharides. Disaccharides are two monosaccharides joined by covalent bonds. Sucrose, common table sugar, is a disaccharide consisting of glucose and fructose. Oligosaccharides, or *few sugars*, are chains of 3 to 20 monosaccharides.

- Include cellulose (sel´-yuh-los), an indigestible substance that provides bulk to the contents of the digestive tract and promotes healthy movement through the intestines

  ✔ **Note:** Polysaccharides, or *many sugars*, may consist of several thousand monosaccharide molecules. Cellulose is a nearly straight polysaccharide found in the cell walls of plants. Other polysaccharides include glycogen (gli´-kuh-juhn) and starches, which are described below.

- Include glycogen, which consists of a very-complex chain of glucose molecules that can be stored in the liver and skeletal muscles until converted back into glucose

- Include starches, which consist of chains of glucose that are split apart during digestion

b. Lipids

- Consist of carbon, hydrogen, and sometimes phosphorus (faws´-fruhs), often in the form of fatty acids

- Include triglycerides (tri-glis´-uh-rids), which store energy primarily in the form of body fat

  ✔ **Note:** True fats consist of a molecule of glycerol and one, two, or three molecules of fatty acids. Triglycerides have three fatty-acid molecules. These lipids are stored between the skin and muscles and around certain organs. When the intake of nutrients does not supply enough energy, the fat can be converted into glucose and used to produce energy.

- Include phospholipids (faws-fo-lip´-uhds), which are one constituent of cell membranes

  ✔ **Note:** Lipids with two fatty acids and a phosphate group (a phosphorus atom with four atoms of oxygen, PO_4) are referred to as *phospholipids*. They help to form walls and sheaths around cells in various structural configurations of molecules.

- Include steroids (stir´-oids), which are one constituent of cell membranes and assist with hormone synthesis

  ✔ **Note:** Steroids differ in structure from other lipids in that they do not consist of glycerol and fatty acids. Instead, they contain four rings of carbon with hydrogen and other molecules attached. Steroids include cholesterol (kuh-les´-tuh-rol) and certain hormones.

- Include prostaglandins (praws-tuh-glan´-duhns), which regulate hormone action, enhance the immune system, and affect the **inflammatory response**

  ✔ **Note:** There are several types of prostaglandins, each of which is a structural variation of a 20-carbon fatty acid with a 5-carbon ring. Prostaglandins originate in virtually every type of tissue. They perform a specific purpose—usually causing a certain chemical reaction, such as aiding in the clotting of blood, increasing the body's response to disease, influencing blood pressure, and various other roles.

c. Proteins

- Consist of amino (uh-me´-no) acids, which are made of carbon, hydrogen, oxygen, nitrogen, and in some cases, sulfur

  ✔ **Note:** Amino acids are chemical structures that include an amine group (NH_2) and a carboxyl group (COOH). There are 20 different amino acids. Amino acids bind to each other through what is called *peptide bonds*. Short chains of amino acids are referred to as *polypeptides* (pawl-i-pep´-tids).

- Include keratin, collagen, hemoglobin, myosin, and other structural proteins that form receptor sites in cell membranes

  ✔ **Note:** One of the more-important structural functions of proteins is to create receptor sites and **pores** in the cell walls. The receptor sites allow certain molecules and other chemical structures to attach to the cell wall. For example, red blood cells have receptor sites for oxygen in the hemoglobin (he´-muh-glo-buhn) protein in their walls. Keratin (ker´-uht-uhn) is found in the skin and hair, while collagen (kawl´-uh-juhn) is part of the tendons and ligaments. Myosin (mi´-uh-suhn) is found in muscles and aid in the contraction or drawing up of working muscles.

- Include hormones, which regulate body functions including growth, **sexual maturation**, and cell functions

- Include **antibodies**, which tag harmful substances in the body so that they will be destroyed

- Include **enzymes**, which serve as catalysts in chemical reactions

d. Nucleic acids

- Consist of nucleotides, which are made of a pentose sugar, a phosphate group, and one of five base chemicals that include nitrogen

  ✔ **Note:** The base chemicals included in nucleotides (nu´-kle-uh-tids) are adenine (ad´-uhn-en), cytosine (sit´-uh-sen), guanine (gwawn´-en), thymine (thi´-men), and uracil (yur´-uh-sil). The pentose sugars are either ribose or deoxyribose.

- Include deoxyribonucleic (de-awk´-si-ri-bo-nu-kle-ik) acid, which is a double strand of nucleotides with a structure that defines the code of inherited traits

  ✔ **Note:** Deoxyribonucleic acid (DNA) consists of two strands of nucleotides that are twisted in a double helix, somewhat like a ladder that has been rotated while one end was held in place. The strands of nucleotides are alternating molecules of phosphate and deoxyribose sugar. The "rungs" of the ladder are pairs of the base chemicals adenine, thymine, cytosine, and guanine. Adenine is always paired with thymine and cytozine is always paired with guanine. The sequence of the base pairs in a strand of DNA is what creates the coded information for assembling the organism. The sequence of code for one protein is called a *gene*.

- Include ribonucleic (ri-bo-nu-kle´-ik) acid, which is a single strand of nucleotides that synthesizes protein

  ✔ **Note:** Ribose combines with a phosphate group and four bases (adenine, cytosine, guanine, and uracil) to form ribonucleic acid (RNA). The nucleotides are joined in a single strand. RNA is formed from DNA in the cells. There are two functional types of RNA. Messenger RNA (mRNA) is a copy of the genetic code from the DNA, while transfer RNA (tRNA) builds proteins by aligning the amino acids correctly.

OBJECTIVE 13

Major elements and compounds that compose the body

a. More than 20 elements are found in the human body.

b. Oxygen is the most-common element in the body by total weight, at approximately 65 percent.

  ✔ **Note:** Because oxygen is a major part of water molecules and 60 to 75 percent of body weight is water, plus the fact that many other compounds contain oxygen, this element is the most common.

c. Carbon, at nearly 19 percent, and hydrogen, at nearly 10 percent, are the other large constituents.

  ✔ **Note:** Carbon and hydrogen are large constituents of the body's composition because they are found in carbohydrates.

d. There are also minor quantities of nitrogen, calcium, and phosphorus.

  ✔ **Note:** Elements such as sodium, magnesium, sulfur, chlorine, and potassium make up less than 1 percent each.

e. There are trace amounts—less than 0.1 percent—of a number of minerals, including manganese, iron, cobalt, copper, zinc, and others, as well as iodine and chlorine.

| OBJECTIVE 14 | **Types of solutions** |

a. Isotonic (i-suh-tawn´-ik)—A solution that has the same concentration of dissolved particles as the solution to which it is compared

✔ **Note:** The prefix *iso-* means "the same." Isotonic solutions are sometimes referred to as *normal solutions* because they are in a state of balance with the compared solution. A fundamental law of physics is that if two solutions are placed in a relationship in which they can exchange material with each other, they will tend to end up with the same concentrations of dissolved materials. The two solutions would be isotonic with each other. This is the condition of blood cells and plasma with regard to the dissolved substances in both. The concentration of dissolved minerals inside the cells is normally the same as that in the plasma, thus there is no flow between the internal and external solutions (see Figure 2 below).

b. Hypertonic (hi-puhr-tawn´-ik)—A solution that has a higher concentration of dissolved particles than the solution to which it is compared

✔ **Note:** If there is a difference in the concentrations of two solutions that have a relationship in which they can exchange material with each other, the solvent will flow toward the higher concentration of solute so that the concentration is reduced in the hypertonic solution. Therefore, if the concentration of the solution surrounding the cells is greater than that of the cells, material will flow out of the cell to the surrounding solution causing the cell to shrink and be destroyed (crenation). See Figure 3 below.

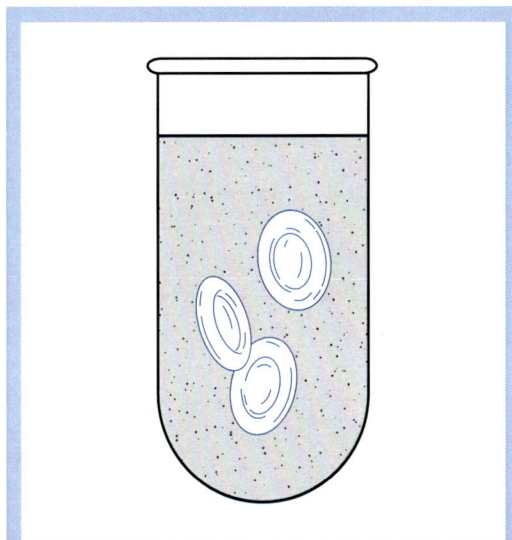

Figure 2
Types of solutions: Isotonic

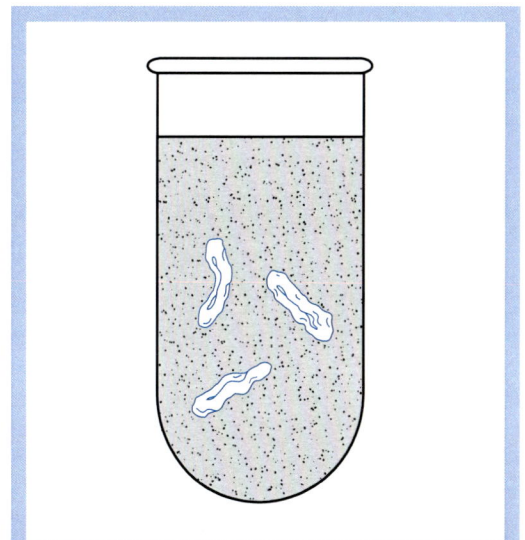

Figure 3
Types of solutions: Hypertonic

c. Hypotonic (hi-po-tawn´-ik)—A solution that has a lower concentration of dissolved particles than the solution to which it is compared

✔ **Note:** If there is a difference in the concentrations of two solutions that have a relationship in which they can exchange material with each other, the solvent will flow toward the higher concentration of solute so that the concentration is increased in the hypotonic solution. Therefore, if the concentration in the cells is greater than that in the surrounding solution, the material in the cells ruptures the cells to create an equilibrium in the surrounding solution (see Figure 4 below).

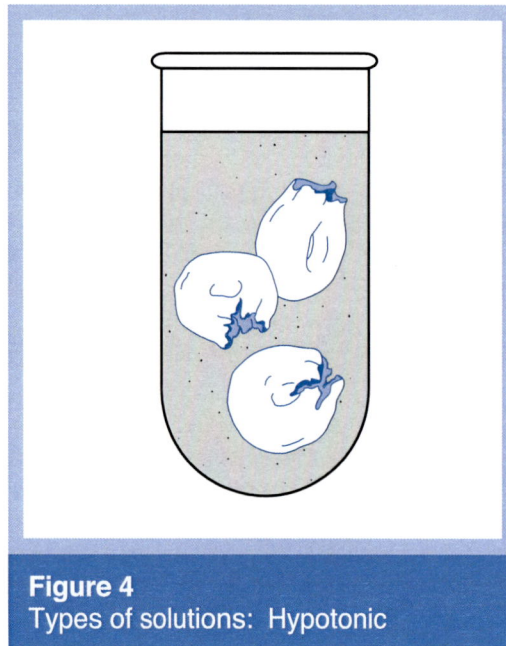

Figure 4
Types of solutions: Hypotonic

OBJECTIVE 15

Major types of fluids in the body

a. Intracellular fluid (in-truh-sel´-yuh-luhr flu´-uhd)—Fluid contained within the cells

b. Interstitial (int-uhr-stish´-uhl) fluid—Fluid between the cells and in special cavities, such as in the cranium

c. Plasma (plaz´-muh)—The fluid portion of blood

✔ **Note:** Plasma composes nearly 60 percent of the volume of blood.

<table>
<tr><td>

OBJECTIVE 16

</td><td>

The term *electrolyte*

KEY TERMS
_____

Acid (as´-uhd)—A substance that releases a hydrogen ion when dissolved

Base (bas´)—A substance that releases a hydroxide ion when dissolved

✔ **Note:** Base substances are also referred to as *alkaline* (al´-kuh-luhn).

Hydroxyl (hi-drawk´-suhl)—An anion consisting of one hydrogen atom and one oxygen atom

✔ **Note:** Hydroxyls can be considered to be the most-basic compound, while a hydrogen cation is the most-acidic. Note that combining the hydrogen cation (H^+) with a hydroxyl anion or *hydroxide ion* (OH^-) forms water (H_2O). In fact, in the body, many chemical reactions involving water are reversible breakdowns of water into H^+ and OH^- and conversion back again into water.

Ion (i´-awn)—An atom or group of atoms with either a positive or a negative electrical charge

✔ **Note:** An atom that has fewer electrons than protons has a positive charge and is called a *positive ion* or *cation* (kat´-i-uhn). an atom that has more electrons than protons has a negative charge and is called a *negative ion* or *anion* (an´-i-uhn). The charge of an ion can play an important role in the transport of chemicals throughout the body.

Salt (sawlt´)—A class of chemicals that have a positive ion other than hydrogen and a negative ion that is not a **hydroxyl**

✔ **Note:** Table salt is sodium chloride and consists of a sodium cation and an anion of chlorine. Numerous other salts exist, many of which play a role in body functioning.

Electrolyte—A substance that forms **ions** when it dissolves

✔ **Note:** Electrolytes include **salts**, **acids**, and **bases** found throughout the body. The fact that the ions have a positive or negative charge provides the body with a mechanism for moving these substances from one place to another, as ions with similar charges tend to move away from each other while those with different charges tend to move toward each other.

</td></tr>
<tr><td>

OBJECTIVE 17

</td><td>

Role of electrolytes in human health

a. Dissolved electrolytes have an excess or shortage of electrons, giving them a negative or a positive charge respectively.

✔ **Note:** Some of the more-common positive electrolytes in the body are sodium (Na^+), potassium (K^+), manganese (Mg^{+2}), and calcium (Ca^{+2}). The most-common negative electrolytes are chloride (Cl^-), phosphate (HPO_4^{-2}), protein anions, and sulfate (SO_4^{-2}). These substances are present in plasma and tissue fluids, though their normal concentration varies from fluid to fluid.

</td></tr>
</table>

b. Body functions are most efficient when the concentrations of the electrolytes are within specific ranges.

✔ **Note:** Tissue fluid and plasma normally have high concentrations of sodium and chloride and low concentrations of potassium, manganese, and phosphate and protein ions with low concentrations of sodium and chloride. These concentration levels are vital to the functions that are performed by tissues and organs.

c. Electrolytes are lost through sweating and through the elimination of urine and feces.

OBJECTIVE 18 **Role of acids and bases in human health**

a. Acids and bases are classed as strong, using a value called pH, with the most-acidic substances having a value toward 0 and the most-basic substances having a value toward 14.

✔ **Note:** The pH scale represents the potential hydrogen that a substance can accommodate. Thus, the 0 end of the scale shows that a hydrogen ion shows no reaction with another hydrogen ion, while a hydroxide ion at the 14 end of the scale will easily react with a hydrogen ion to form water. At the midpoint of the scale is pure water with a value of 7, showing that it is neither acidic nor alkaline.

b. Body fluids have a normal pH value with a narrow range above and below that value.

✔ **Note:** The normal pH of blood is 7.35 to 7.45, meaning that it is slightly alkaline. Intracellular fluid has a pH of approximately 6.8 or slightly more-acidic than pure water.

c. If the pH value of a fluid goes above or below its ideal range, chemical reactions will be affected.

d. Normal human activities can lead to major shifts in pH.

✔ **Note:** Changes in diet, changes in exercise, environmental exposures, and illness can affect the pH balance in the body. However, normal cell respiration would also lead to an increase in acidity if the body did not have mechanisms to compensate for such changes.

e. To compensate for these potential changes in pH, the body contains buffer systems.

✔ **Note:** There are three major buffer systems: the bicarbonate system associated with respiration, the phosphate system associated with the kidneys, and the protein system associated with intracellular fluid.

f. Buffer systems contain a weak acid and a weak base that react with strong acids and strong bases to produce substances that do not change the normal pH excessively.

OBJECTIVE 19

The term _metabolism_

KEY TERMS

Anabolism (uh-nab´-uh-liz-uhm)—The process of chemical synthesis in which smaller molecules are combined to produce larger molecules

Catabolism (kuh-tab´-uh-liz-uhm)—The process of reducing large molecules into smaller molecules

✔ **Note:** Anabolism requires energy to create the bonds and generally a catalyst such as an enzyme. Catabolism generally releases energy but also requires catalysts. Together, the two processes make up metabolism.

Metabolism—The processes that lead to chemical reactions in the body

✔ **Note:** Chemical reactions take place because of the natural interactions of specific substances, due to the addition of energy such as heat, or because of the presence of catalysts. A chemical reaction may either break chemicals down into other substances and energy or bond substances together. Metabolism can result either in **catabolism** or **anabolism**. Both types of reactions are required for good health. For example, anabolism can lead to the formation of muscle and bone. Catabolism can result in the release of energy from nutrients.

OBJECTIVE 20

Use of energy by the body

✔ **Note:** One of the laws of physics is that energy and matter cannot be created or destroyed. They can only be converted between different forms. This is a key concept in understanding metabolism. Matter is converted into other types of matter and into energy. The energy is converted into matter—cells and other components of the body—and into other types of energy, such as the contraction of muscles so that a person can move.

a. The primary source of energy in the body is adenosine triphosphate (uh-den´-uh-sen tri´-faws-fat) (ATP).

   ✔ **Note:** ATP is composed of ribose, adenine, and three phosphate molecules. Adenine (ad´-un-en) is a molecule with five nitrogen and three hydrogen atoms. A molecule with the same structure as ATP except with one less phosphate group occurs naturally in cells and is called _adenosine diphosphate_ (uh-den´-uh-sen di´-faws-fat) (ADP).

b. During cell metabolism in which glucose and oxygen are converted into carbon dioxide and water, some of the energy released creates a bond between ADP and a phosphate group to produce ATP.

c. Energy is stored in the phosphate bonds of ATP until it is needed for cell functions.

d. All cells contain enzymes that allow them to break the phosphate bonds in ATP.

   ✔ **Note:** The phosphate bonds are known as _high-energy bonds_. When they are broken, a relatively large amount of energy is released in the cell.

---

e. Energy released from ATP fuels cell functions, including cell division to produce new cells.

f. Some of the energy is applied to moving substances in and out of the cell and in carrying out chemical reactions, as well as providing the cell with a stable temperature.

OBJECTIVE 21

Characteristics of body temperature

a. Normal body temperature ranges from 96.5° F to 99.5° F (36° C to 38° C).

✔ **Note:** Body temperature normally varies 1 to 2 degrees during a 24-hour period.

b. Normal temperature is considered to be 98.6° F (37° C).

✔ **Note:** Body-temperature regulation in infants is not as precise due to their small amount of skin-surface area. Body-temperature regulation in older adults is not as precise due to reduced efficiency in the mechanisms that regulate body temperature.

c. Temperature is normally lower during sleep.

d. Body temperature is regulated by the hypothalamus.

e. Blood vessels near the surface of the skin constrict to reduce heat loss.

f. Blood vessels near the surface of the skin dilate to increase heat loss.

✔ **Note:** Although most heat loss occurs through the skin, heat loss also occurs through exhaling breath (respiration). There is also a slight amount of heat loss through the elimination of body wastes through urination and defecation.

g. Heat is removed from the body by sweating.

h. Fever is an abnormally high body temperature.

✔ **Note:** Fever is generally the result of a disruption of the body-temperature regulation mechanisms due to injury or illness.

i. Hypothermia is an abnormally low body temperature.

✔ **Note:** Hypothermia is generally the result of exposure to low environmental temperatures such as exposure to cold air or water.

| OBJECTIVE 22 | **Basic activities that define life** |

> KEY TERMS
>
> **Asexual** (a-sek´-shuhl)—Relating to reproduction that does not involve the union of individual organisms or separate cells
>
> ✔ **Note:** Asexual reproduction occurs in the simplest life forms, such as one-celled organisms, and at the cellular level in higher life forms when internal cells divide to reproduce.
>
> **Sexual** (sek´-shuhl)—Relating to reproduction that requires a union of two organisms or the union of separate cells
>
> **Theory of evolution** (ev-uh-lu´-shuhn)—A theory that proposes that all life began as simple organic compounds that over time developed the characteristics of life and continued to become more complex in functioning and in coping with the environment

✔ **Note:** You have seen that our bodies consist of various assemblies of common chemicals and that most of what happens within our bodies are simply reactions among those chemicals. So what distinguishes us from other groups of chemicals, such as rocks? Scientists generally define life by the activities that are common in living organisms and are not normally found in nonliving things.

a. Reproduction (re-pruh-duhk´-shuhn)—The process by which organisms create more of their own kind

   ✔ **Note:** Living organisms must have a way of renewing themselves because all living things break down or fall victim to injury so that they eventually die. Through reproduction, a cell can divide to make a replacement or a man and a woman can have children. Reproduction may be **sexual** or **asexual**.

b. Growth (groth´)—The orderly increase in size that an organism exhibits as it matures

   ✔ **Note:** Living things tend to get bigger as they age to the point of maturity. Even single-celled organisms double in size from a divided cell or grow from a spore or cyst.

c. Metabolism (muh-tab´-uh-liz-uhm)—The process by which organisms convert matter and energy to sustain life functions

   ✔ **Note:** It takes energy to sustain life. Organisms find this energy in nutritional matter or in the environment. For example, humans eat food and convert the food to energy and chemicals required to support the functions of life. Many plants are able to use the energy of sunlight to sustain life. Metabolism includes those internal processes that allow an organism to derive energy and the chemicals required to support life functions from external sources.

d. Movement (muv´-muhnt)—The ability to change the location of matter from one place to another

✔ **Note:** While it is fairly obvious that human beings and most animals travel from place to place, it may be less apparent that a tree exhibits movement or that a barnacle attached to a rock moves. Many plants turn their flowers or leaves toward the sun. Even in plants where such movement is absent, there is a flow of nutrients and water through the plant, just as blood flows through the human body. Thus, movement may be either external or internal.

e. Responsiveness (ri-spawn´-siv-nes)—The characteristic of an organism to react to changes in its environment

✔ **Note:** Even simple organisms are equipped with sense organs that provide the organism with an awareness of its environment. Often these environmental conditions will cause a reaction in the organism, as when you pull your hand away from a hot object. The response may be done either consciously, such as eating to relieve hunger, or automatically, such as the constriction of the pupil of the eye when exposed to bright light.

f. Adaptation (ad-ap-ta´-shuhn)—The process of modifying life processes to improve an organism's chances of survival

✔ **Note:** Adaptation may appear to be very similar to responsiveness, and the two are related. However, responsiveness generally refers to changes in the organism's behavior that cope immediately with a change in the environment, where adaptation often indicates a long-term change. Adaptation may occur for an individual, as when a snowshoe rabbit turns white in the winter, or for a species, as suggested by the **theory of evolution**.

OBJECTIVE 23 | **Cell theory**

KEY TERM

Protoplasm (prot´-uh-plaz-uhm)—The complex mass of proteins and other organic and inorganic materials that is capable of exhibiting the characteristics of life

---

All organisms are made of small, enclosed bodies called cells and of the products of those cells.

✔ **Note:** Cells are small bits of organized **protoplasm** encased in a thickened membrane. In multicellular organisms, cells tend to have a specialized function that contributes to the overall functioning of the organism.

OBJECTIVE 24

Functions of the compounds found in protoplasm

a. Water—Serves as the solvent in all cell chemistry

✔ **Note:** Water not only makes up most of the body, but it is also involved in virtually every chemical reaction that takes place in the body. About 65 percent of the water in the body is contained within cells. However, the water within the body is in constant motion, transporting molecules in and out of the cells and moving substances about the body through the bloodstream and lymphatic vessels. The transported chemicals are generally in solution.

b. Protein—Forms the structural framework of protoplasm

c. Carbohydrates—Serve as a source of energy during metabolism

d. Fats—Store excess energy

✔ **Note:** The energy provided by nutrients that is not required by the body immediately is converted to fat and stored between the skin and muscles.

e. Nucleic acids—Control the growth and reproduction of cells

f. Mineral salts—Serve as chemical buffers to maintain the chemical balance in cells

✔ **Note:** Salts serve as a source of trace elements and are needed in the cells in small quantities. For example, the formation of ATP requires that phosphate molecules be available in the cell. One source of phosphates is the mineral salt calcium phosphate.

OBJECTIVE 25

Principal types of protoplasm

a. Nucleoplasm (nu´-kle-uh-plaz-uhm)—The protoplasm found in the nucleus of a cell

✔ **Note:** All human cells except mature red blood cells have a nucleus.

b. Cytoplasm (sit´-uh-plaz-uhm)—The protoplasm found outside the nucleus of a cell

OBJECTIVE 26	**Major parts of a cell**

✔ **Note:** Cells contain specialized structures that perform specific functions in maintaining the cell as a living body. The exact structures and their arrangements will vary from cell to cell depending on the type of parent organism, the cell's role within the parent organism, and the cell's stage of life. The cell shown in Figure 5 is representative of cells in general and is not intended to be a specific cell or to reflect the structure of all cells.

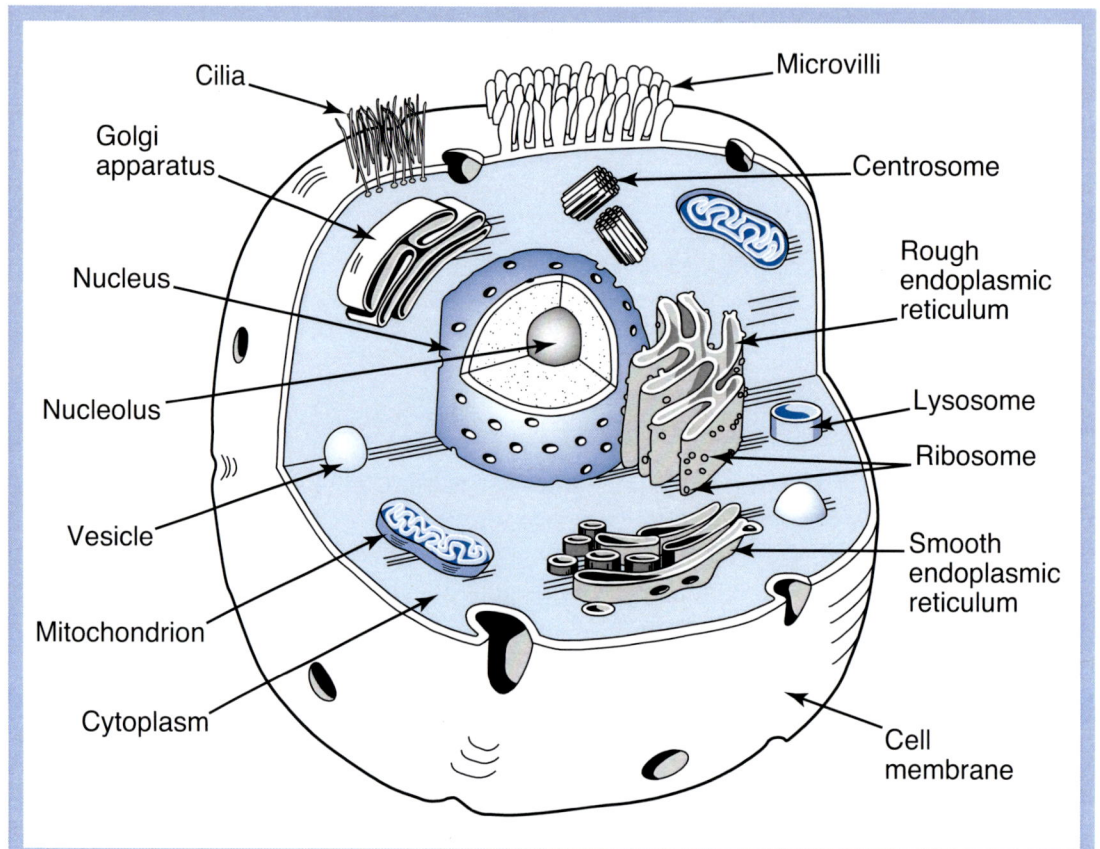

Figure 5
Major parts of a cell

OBJECTIVE **27**	**Functions of the major parts of a cell**

KEY TERM

Permeability (puhr-me-uh-bil´-uht-e)—The characteristic of a material to allow other substances to pass through it

✔ **Note:** An important function of a cell is to take in substances such as oxygen and nutrients and to release substances such as carbon dioxides and enzymes. However, the membrane must prevent substances such as toxins from entering the cell. For this reason, the cell membrane is said to be *selectively permeable*.

---

a. Nucleus—Regulates cellular structure and activities, including reproduction of the cell (see Figure 5)

b. Cell membrane—Allows some molecules to enter the cell while preventing entry by other molecules (see Figure 5)

> ✔ **Note:** The cell membrane is sometimes referred to as the *plasma membrane*. The membrane exhibits selective **permeability**—it selects the chemicals that are allowed to pass through it, permitting some to pass in or out easily and keeping others out completely.

c. Cytoplasm—Provides structure to the cell and supports other parts of the cell (see Figure 5)

> ✔ **Note:** The cytoplasm contains a number of specialized structures referred to as *organelles* (or-guh-nels´). The remaining parts listed in this objective are organelles.

d. Endoplasmic reticulum (en´-duh-plaz-mik re-tik´-yu-luhm)—Provides a passageway for the transport of materials within the cell and synthesizes lipids

> ✔ **Note:** The endoplasmic reticulum winds through the cytoplasm, delivering proteins and other chemicals to various parts of the cell and to other organelles. There are two types of endoplasmic reticula: smooth and rough (see Figure 5 on page 33). The bumpy appearance of rough endoplasmic reticulum is created by the ribosomes—another type of organelle—that attach to it. Smooth endoplasmic reticulum lacks ribosomes.

e. Ribosome (ri´-buh-som)—Synthesizes protein

> ✔ **Note:** The ribosomes are attached to the endoplasmic reticula and are scattered throughout the cell (see Figure 5). The ribosomes contain RNA and play a key role in cell division.

f. Golgi apparatus (gol´-je ap-uh-rat´-uhs)—Synthesizes carbohydrates and packages materials to prepare them for secretion from the cell

✔ **Note:** The Golgi apparatus (see Figure 5) generally lie near the terminal ends of endoplasmic reticula and receive the proteins produced by the endoplasmic reticula and ribosomes. This protein material is delivered in small bubble-like packets called *vesicles* (ves´-i-kuhls) (see Figure 5). In the Golgi apparatus, the proteins are modified for special purposes, such as serving as pores in the cell membrane or as enzymes to be secreted from the cell. Once the proteins have been processed by the Golgi apparatus, they are released in vesicles for transport to their destination.

g. Mitochondrion (mit-uh-kawn´-dre-uhn)—Produces ATP and serves as the site of cell respiration

✔ **Note:** The mitochondria generate the energy required by the cell. They consist of a smooth outer sac that contains an inner sac partitioned by numerous folds called *cristae* (see Figure 5). The mitochondria are rich in fats, proteins, and enzymes. The more energy that a cell requires to perform its functions, the more mitochondria the cell is likely to have.

h. Lysosome (li´-suh-som)—Contains the enzymes used to digest ingested material and damaged tissue (see Figure 5)

i. Centrosome (sen´-truh-som)—Organizes special spindle fibers during cell division

✔ **Note:** Centrosomes consist of two cylinders called *centrioles* (see Figure 5).

OBJECTIVE 28

Major parts of a cell nucleus

a. Nuclear membrane—A thickening of the outer surface of the nucleus protoplasm that regulates the movement of materials into and out of the nucleus

b. Chromosome (kro´-muh-som)—One of several strands of DNA that contains the genetic code that determines inherited traits

✔ **Note:** Human cells contain 23 pairs of chromosomes that carry the genetic code. When a cell is dividing to reproduce itself, the DNA molecules form tight coils so that they have the appearance of short rods. This is the chromosomal state. When the cells are not dividing, the DNA molecules have the appearance of granules or threads in the nucleoplasm and are referred to as *chromatin* (kro´-muht-uhn).

c. Nucleolus (nu-kle´-uh-luhs)—A dense spherical structure within the nucleus that is involved in protein synthesis and that forms ribosomal RNA (see Figure 5)

OBJECTIVE 29

Specialized structures in cells

a. Microvilli (mi-kro-vil´-e)—Extensions of the cell cytoplasm that line the intestines (see Figure 5)

b. Flagellum (fluh-jel´-uhm)—A single hair-like projection on a sperm cell

c. Cilia (sil´-e-uh)—Hair-like projections of the cells that form the mucous lining of the respiratory system and other passageways (see Figure 5)

OBJECTIVE 30	**Functions of the specialized structures in cells**

a. Microvilli—Serve to increase the surface area of cells

> ✔ **Note:** The purpose of the intestines is to absorb nutrients. The reason that the small intestines twist around and fold back on themselves is to increase their length so that food being digested and absorbed will have to travel a greater distance, thus increasing the amount of intestine to which the nutrients are exposed. Microvilli serve the same purpose by presenting "fingers" into the interior of the intestines. This too increases the surface area to which nutrients are exposed.

b. Flagellum—Helps to propel a sperm cell so that it can reach an ovum

> ✔ **Note:** The sperm, or spermatozoa (spuhr-mat-uh-zo´-uh), is the male reproductive cell, while the ovum is the female reproductive cell. When an ovum is released for fertilization in the female, it is still beyond the point where sperm is deposited. This means that the sperm must "swim" the rest of the way to reach the ovum. The flagellum wiggles back and forth and whips around to propel the sperm toward the ovum.

c. Cilia—Help to propel fluid in one direction over the surface of cells

> ✔ **Note:** The cilia act like the bristles of a broom on a microscopic scale. Their sweeping motion moves fluids and transported substances along a passageway. For example, when the ovaries release an egg cell, cilia extending from the cells that line the interior of the fallopian tubes move the ovum toward the uterus. This increases the chances of fertilization by presenting the ovum to sperm cells and then to the uterus to be implanted or to be discharged if not fertilized.

OBJECTIVE 31	**Functions of a cell**

a. To absorb materials to support cell functions

   Examples: Oxygen, nutrients

b. To metabolize nutrients

c. To metabolize oxygen

d. To release energy

e. To synthesize protein

f. To excrete waste products

g. To reproduce itself

h. To support functions specific to that kind of cell

> ✔ **Note:** The body contains hundreds of types of cells that serve specialized functions to support the purposes of the organ system in which the cells originate. The set of objectives in this module concentrates on the structure and chemistry of cells in general. The details of specific cell functioning will be provided in the modules that deal with the individual organ systems.

Module 2-A: Biochemistry and Microbiology

OBJECTIVE 32	**The term** *transport*

Transport—The movement of substances in and out of the cells

✔ **Note:** Depending on the type of cell, the substance, and the purpose of the movement, the method of transport can vary in a number of ways. However, the process can be generally divided into two categories: passive and active (see Objective 33).

OBJECTIVE 33 — **The terms** *active transport* **and** *passive transport*

a. Passive transport—Movement that occurs without any energy being expended by the cell

✔ **Note:** In passive transport, chemicals move through the cell wall due to the mechanics of solutions. You have previously studied a general principle of fluid mechanics that states if two solutions are placed in a relationship in which materials can move between them, then there will be a flow of solvent from the area of lower concentration to the area of higher concentration until an isotonic state is reached. The word *passive* means that an action takes place without resistance to outside forces.

b. Active transport—Movement that requires the use of energy for the cell to transport the material through the cell wall

✔ **Note:** Active transport goes counter to the normal mechanics of solution. In other words, the solvent flows from the area of higher concentration to the area of lower concentration, causing the higher concentration to become even greater and the lower concentration to decrease further. This is somewhat like water running uphill. For active transport to take place, the cell must expend energy.

OBJECTIVE 34 — **Types of passive transport**

a. Diffusion (dif-yu´-zhuhn)—The process by which particles in a fluid spread throughout the fluid to produce an equal concentration

✔ **Note:** Diffusion is the process that involves the flow of a substance from an area of higher concentration to one of lower concentration. Although this process is described as *passive*, all movement requires some form of energy. In this case, the energy is that of the atoms that make up the substance. The electrons that orbit the nucleus, the differences in electrical charges, and other forces cause atoms to be in continuous motion. In a solid, the movement is very slow. However, if a solid is dissolved in a liquid, many of the bonds that hold the substance in its solid shape are broken and the atoms and molecules of the substance move about with more freedom, bouncing off each other to further add to the motion. Substances in gaseous states are even more free to move about, which explains why an odor can so quickly fill a room.

b. Osmosis (awz-mo´-suhs)—The process by which solvent molecules pass through a semipermeable membrane to produce an equal concentration on each side of the membrane

✔ **Note:** Osmosis is actually a form of diffusion, one that involves a semi-permeable or selectively permeable membrane. With osmosis, the emphasis is on the substances that are allowed to pass through the membrane. Similarly, filtration (see below) can be a form of osmosis in which the emphasis is on the prevention of movement of select substances. An example of osmosis is the flow of fluid into a cell if the electrolyte concentration within the cell gets too high.

c. Filtration (fil-tra´-shuhn)—The process by which solvents or specific particles are able to move through a membrane that prevents the passage of other solvents or particles

✔ **Note:** There are several filter systems in the body besides the cell walls. For example, the spleen filters blood that passes through it. Filtration requires force to move the solution through the filter. That force may be normal fluid mechanics forces or it may be an active force such as the heart pumping blood through the spleen.

OBJECTIVE 35 | **Types of active transport**

a. Physiological pump—The process that moves molecules or ions through cell membranes against the pressure of natural forces

✔ **Note:** A physiological pump may be an organ like the heart. In active cell transport, the most-common form of physiological pump is a "carrier" molecule to which substances attach and are then carried in or out of the cell by movement of the carrier. An example is the sodium-potassium pump, which uses a molecule of sodium-potassium ATP to carry sodium ions out of the cells and potassium into the cells.

b. Phagocytosis (fag-uh-si-to´-suhs)—The process of a cell engulfing a solid particle with a portion of its membrane, which then breaks off from the membrane and migrates into the cell as a closed vesicle

✔ **Note:** During phagocytosis, the transported substance connects to receptor sites on the surface of the cell. The cell then draws in that portion of the cell wall and pinches it off to form a vesicle. The vesicle can then be moved about the cytoplasm as required. The same mechanism is used for pinocytosis (see below) except that the process involves a liquid rather than a solid. Phagocytosis and pinocytosis are sometimes collectively referred to as *endocytosis* (en-duh-si-to´-suhs) because materials are transported into the cell.

c. Pinocytosis (pin-uh-si-to´-suhs)—The process of a cell engulfing a liquid particle with a portion of its membrane, which then breaks off from the membrane and migrates into the cell as a closed vesicle

d. Exocytosis (ek-so-si-to´-suhs)—The process of a cell carrying substances in vesicles and secreting through the cell membrane

✔ **Note:** Exocytosis has previously been described in Objective 27 as part of the function of Golgi apparatus.

Module 2-A: Biochemistry and Microbiology

OBJECTIVE 36 | **Process of cell growth**

> KEY TERM
> _____
>
> **Self-replication** (self´ rep-luh-ka´-shuhn)—To produce a copy of oneself
>
> ✔ **Note:** Cells reproduce by replicating themselves and structures with the cells are also capable of dividing to make a copy of the structure. DNA replicates itself by splitting into two strands and then rejoining segments composed of new nucleotides joining each of the existing strands.

a. Once a cell forms, it must produce additional cytoplasm and cell membrane as the cell enlarges.

   ✔ **Note:** New cells are formed by the division of existing cells. This is followed by a growth period called the *interphase* (int´-uhr-faz).

b. Part of the growth process involves protein synthesis through anabolism.

c. During protein synthesis, amino acids are bonded in polypeptide chains.

d. To create the polypeptide chains, a ribosome attaches to a complementary set of RNA molecules—a transfer RNA (tRNA) molecule and a messenger RNA (mRNA) strand—and holds them together during protein synthesis.

   ✔ **Note:** The messenger RNA carries the genetic code that describes the type of protein to be constructed. The transfer RNA attracts amino acids based on the coding in the messenger RNA.

e. The amino acids are drawn to the ribosome.

f. The ribosome secretes an enzyme that promotes the formation of a peptide bond.

g. The ribosome moves along the RNA strand pair building polypeptides.

h. In some cases, after the ribosome travels the full length of the RNA strands and moves on, enzymes present in the cell connect the polypeptides to form proteins.

i. Other enzymes cause the proteins to form cell membrane and organelles.

j. Mitochondria increase by **self-replication**.

k. Just before the cell begins to reproduce, the DNA also replicates itself.

OBJECTIVE 37

Types of cell reproduction

✔ **Note:** Human cells undergo two types of division in order to reproduce. Mitosis (mi-to´-suhs) is the process used by virtually all cells, while meiosis (mi-o´-suhs) occurs only in reproductive cells.

a. Mitosis

- Occurs in all human cells other than reproductive cells and nerve-tissue cells

- Gives rise to two daughter cells that are identical to the parent cell

- Consists of four distinct stages

    ✔ **Note:** The four phases of mitosis are (1) prophase, (2) metaphase, (3) anaphase, and (4) telophase. During prophase (pro´-faz), the cell prepares for division. The chromatids curl into dense chromosomes, the centrioles move to opposite ends (poles) of the cell and spindle fibers extend between them, and the nucleus dissolves. In the metaphase (met´-uh-faz), the spindle fibers have stretched from one end of the cell to the other and the chromosomes align across the midline of the cell at right angles to the spindle fibers, to which they attach. As the anaphase (an´-uh-faz) begins, the chromosome pairs (called *centromeres* [sen´-truh-mirz]) split and migrate toward opposite poles. The split of the centromeres results in the cell having sets of identical chromosomes in each half with each half having the same number of chromosomes as the original cell, and the cell begins to pinch in at the midline between the two poles. The final phase, or telophase (tel´-uh-faz), completes reproductive division by reversing the processes of the prophase in each half of the parent cell. A nucleus develops in each half, the chromosomes revert back to chromatids, and the spindle fibers disappear. Once these structures are all in place, the two halves split and two daughter cells exist in place of the split parent cell.

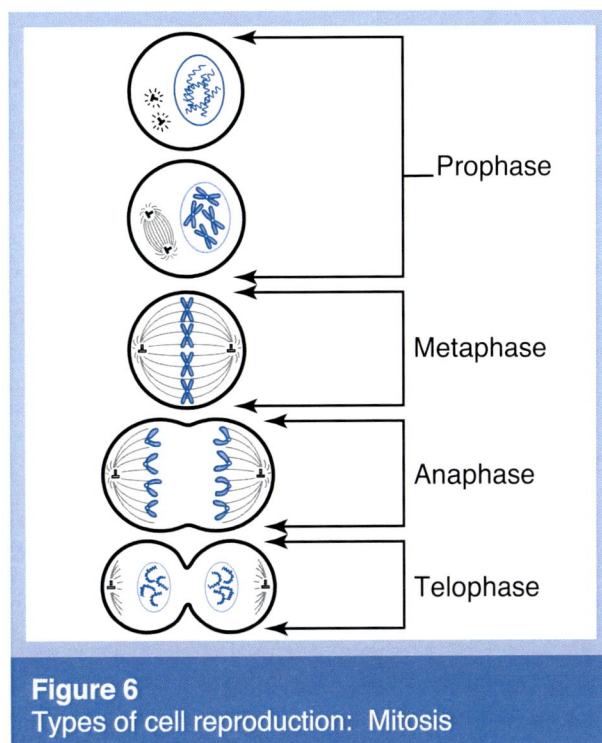

Figure 6
Types of cell reproduction: Mitosis

b.   Meiosis

- Occurs in reproductive cells

- Gives rise to four daughter cells that each contain only half the number of chromosomes found in the parent cell

- Consists of two stages

  ✔ **Note:** The purpose of meiosis is to create reproductive cells that have only one half of the number of chromosomes normally found in the organism's cells. In this way, when the two reproductive cells unite, the resulting cell will have a full set of chromosomes. The first stage of meiosis is called *meiosis I* and begins with normal mitosis. In *meiosis II*, the process is repeated so that by the end of the second telophase, four cells have been produced. However, as the second stage begins, the two cells do not replicate their chromosomes as is done at the beginning of mitosis. Thus, the four cells produced have only half the number of chromosomes normally found in the organism's cells. The resulting cells are generally referred to as *gametes* (gam´-ets), though for male reproductive cells the process begins with spermatogonia (spuhr-mat-uh-go´-ne-uh) and produces spermatozoa and the process for female reproductive cells begins with oogonia (o-uh-go´-ne-uh) and produces one ootid and three polar bodies. The ootid has more cytoplasm than the polar bodies, which eventually disintegrate. This is something of a simplification of the two processes, but they will be discussed in more detail in later modules.

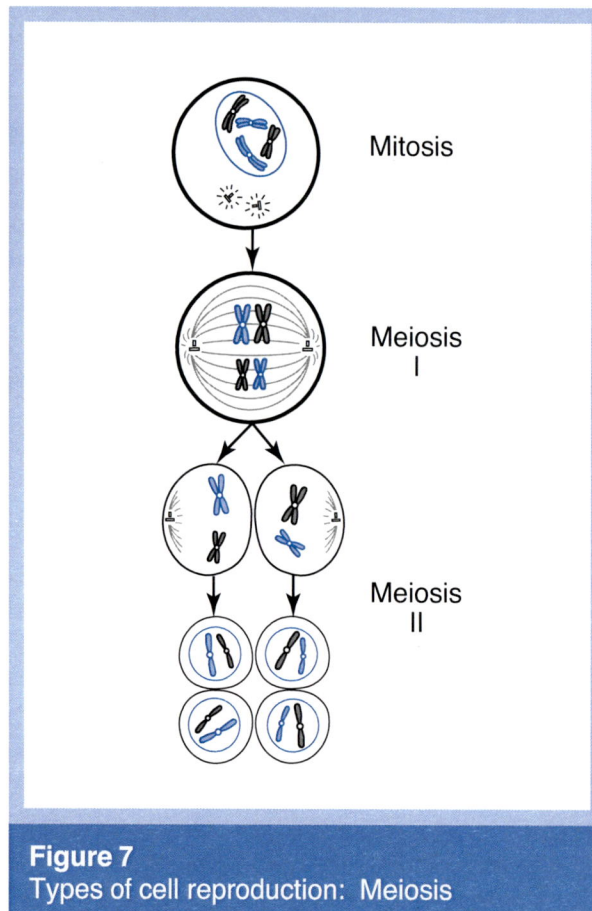

Figure 7
Types of cell reproduction: Meiosis

OBJECTIVE 38	**Process in which the genetic makeup of a cell can be changed**

a. Exposure to certain conditions can disrupt the genetic makeup of a cell, resulting in a mutation.

✔ **Note:** Conditions that cause mutations are called *mutagens.* The world around us is full of mutagens, some natural and some produced by human activities. Some mutations may be beneficial, which is part of the basis of the theory of evolution, which suggests that mutations that help an organism to adapt and survive are likely to be passed on to the organism's offspring. However, some mutations harm the organism or lessen its chances of survival.

b. A mutation may lead to structural or functional disorders that are then passed on to daughter cells during mitosis.

✔ **Note:** Many mutations are not passed on because the afflicted organism does not survive to reproduce or the mutation itself may leave the organism unable to reproduce. A number of mutations have been assimilated into the genetic code of individuals. For example, some persons are unable to see colors or are unable to distinguish between certain colors such as red and green and are said to be *color-blind.* Color-blindness is an inherited trait that probably started as a mutation. The condition sickle-cell anemia is an inherited condition in which a person's red blood cells are misshapen. Sickle-cell anemia probably began as a mutation. Cancer is also a common outcome of changes in the genetic makeup of cells. Cancer, which includes more than 100 varieties in humans, is always characterized by abnormal cell functioning. Malignant cancers exhibit uncontrolled cell division.

OBJECTIVE 39	**Sources of mutation-causing conditions**

a. Exposure to chemicals

Examples: Inhaling asbestos; inhaling the tar that enters the lungs from smoking cigarettes

✔ **Note:** You know by now that our bodies are basically chemical containers in which reactions are taking place continuously. It should come as no surprise then that the introduction of foreign chemicals into the body can disrupt those reactions, including the reactions that transfer the genetic code. Such exposures may lead to illnesses, but they may also directly affect the genetic makeup of the cells.

b. Exposure to energy sources

Examples: Exposure to radioactive materials; exposure to the ultraviolet light of the sun

✔ **Note:** Most skin cancers are the result of exposure to ultraviolet light. The energies emitted by radioactive materials can penetrate deep into the body and cause mutations in the genetic code. These energies can even reach the ova and sperm stored in the body and developing fetuses to cause mutations in offspring that did not result from the inheritance of those mutations through the genetic codes of the parents.

c. Infections by other organisms

Example: Viruses that disrupt cell reproduction

✔ **Note:** Illness and infectious organisms may create chemical imbalances or toxic conditions in the body that disrupt normal reproduction.

OBJECTIVE 40   **Types of cellular respiration**

✔ **Note:** Cell respiration is that part of metabolism that specifically deals with the conversion of glucose to produce energy in the cells (see Figure 8 on the next page). There are three types of cellular respiration: (1) glycolysis (gli-kawl´-uh-suhs), (2) aerobic oxidation (ar-o´-bik awk-suh-da´-shuhn), and (3) electron transport system.

a. Glycolysis (anaerobic oxidation)

- Uses enzymes located in the cytoplasm

- Does not require oxygen

  ✔ **Note:** *Anaerobic* means "without air or oxygen." Glycolysis does not use oxygen in its reaction. This is helpful to the cells if there is not enough oxygen available, as might occur with respiratory diseases or strenuous exercise.

- Requires two molecules of ATP to start the reaction

- Converts glucose and two ATP molecules into four ATP molecules, hydrogen, and energy

  ✔ **Note:** Glycolysis produces pyruvic (pi-ru´-vik) acid and, in a continuing reaction in the absence of oxygen, lactic (lak´-tik) acid. The lactic acid can later be converted back into pyruvic acid or glucose.

- Requires the vitamin niacin

- May develop into aerobic oxidation once oxygen is available

  ✔ **Note:** Once glucose has been converted into pyruvic acid, glycolysis can follow one of two paths. If there is still a shortage of oxygen, the reaction will continue along the path to produce lactic acid. However, if oxygen is available, the pyruvic acid will move to the mitochondria to be used in aerobic oxidation.

b. Aerobic oxidation

  ✔ **Note:** Aerobic oxidation is also called *Krebs cycle* or *citric-acid cycle*.

- Uses enzymes located in the mitochondria

- Requires oxygen

- Converts pyruvic acid into one ATP molecule, hydrogen, carbon dioxide, and carbon molecules

- Requires the vitamins thiamine, riboflavin, and niacin

- May continue through additional cycles as carbon combines with acetyl coenzyme A (uh-set´-uhl ko-en´-zim a)

c. Electron transport system

✔ **Note:** The electron transport system is also referred to as the *cytochrome* (sit´-uh-krom) *transport system*.

- Uses proteins located in the mitochondria

- Allows the electrons released by hydrogen atoms to react with cytochromes to generate enough energy to produce 34 ATP molecules from each glucose molecule

- Combines hydrogen and oxygen released from other forms of respiration to produce water

- Requires the vitamins riboflavin and niacin and the minerals iron or copper

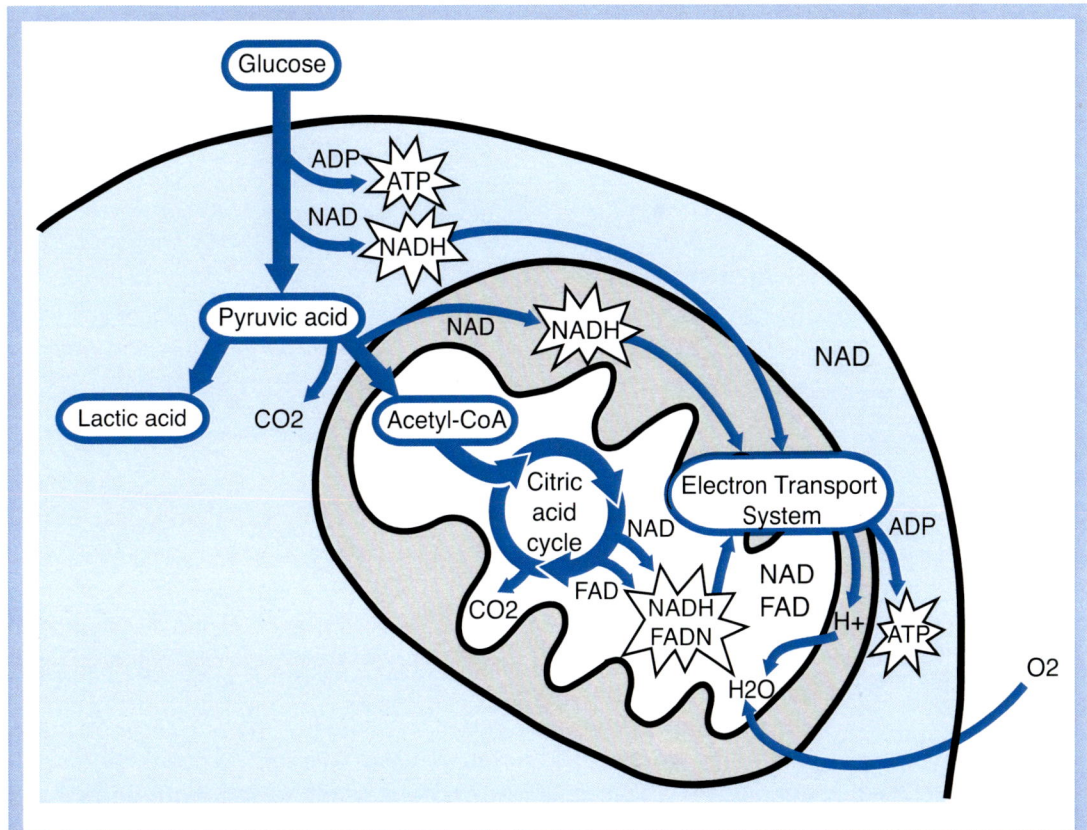

Figure 8
Cell respiration

Module 2-A: Biochemistry and Microbiology

OBJECTIVE 41

Levels in the taxonomy system used to classify organisms

✔ **Note:** Scientists use a system called *taxonomy* to classify all organisms based on their similarities and differences. The system contains seven major levels, beginning with the very broadest similarities and getting more specific until a single kind of organism is identified.

a. Kingdom

✔ **Note:** There are two major kingdoms: plants and animals. As advances in technologies have enabled scientists to discover more about microbiology and biochemistry, other kingdoms have been added, including fungi, protists (including most algae), and monera (including bacteria). Humans are classed in the animal kingdom.

b. Phylum

Example: The human phylum is Chordata.

c. Class

Example: The human class is Mammalia.

d. Order

Example: The human order is Omnivora.

e. Family

Example: The human family is Primates.

f. Genus

Example: The human genus is Homo.

g. Species

Example: The human species is *Sapiens*.

OBJECTIVE 42

Types of relationships between organisms

✔ **Note:** Because we share the planet with each other, organisms form relationships with each other. Generally, these relationships may be classed as beneficial, harmful, or neutral. For example, you know that certain organisms can cause illness in humans. On the other hand, there are organisms that live in our intestines that help us to digest food. Still other organisms seem to have little or no interaction with humans. The terms presented in this objective describe some of the more-important relationships that can exist between organisms.

a. Symbiosis (sim-bi-o´-suhs)—A relationship between two organisms that have close contact with each other

✔ **Note:** Symbiosis is a general term for any close relationship between organisms of different species, whether that relationship is beneficial or harmful or neither. The two organisms may simply live very near each other, the two organisms may have physical contact, or one organism may actually live on or within the other.

b.   Mutualism (myuch´-uh-wuh-liz-uhm)—A relationship between two organisms that is beneficial to both

✔ **Note:** In a mutualistic relationship, the organisms maintain close contact with one another and both benefit from each other. For example, tick birds stay near herds of cattle or antelope. The birds feed on insects and other pests that bother the herd animals. Thus, both types of organisms benefit. The term *symbiosis* was once applied to this type of relationship but now has a broader meaning.

c.   Commensalism (kuh-men´-suh-liz-uhm)—A relationship between two organisms in which one organism benefits and the other neither benefits nor is harmed

✔ **Note:** The remora fish that attach themselves to sharks, whales, and sea turtles provide no benefit to their hosts yet cause their hosts no real harm. However, the remora is able to eat bits of food that the host misses when feeding. In this way the remora benefits from the commensalistic relationship.

d.   Neutralism (nu´-truh-liz-uhm)—A relationship between two organisms in which the organisms present no significant benefit or harm to each other

✔ **Note:** Squirrels and songbirds that live in the same tree share a neutralistic relationship. While there may be some competition for food and nest sites, the two species have little interaction. In parts of Africa, herds of animals, like zebras and wildebeests, travel and graze together. The increased herd size may allow a greater degree of alertness to danger from predators, but there is essentially no direct benefit to either type of organism.

e.   Parasitism (par´-uh-suh-tiz-uhm)—A relationship between two organisms in which one organism is harmed by the presence of the other

✔ **Note:** Parasitism is an important concern to all health professionals. The organisms that cause diseases in humans are generally parasites. Additionally, disease-carrying organisms such as fleas and ticks are parasitic on humans.

f.   Pathogenic (path´-uh-jen-ik)—A relationship between two organisms in which one organism is capable of causing a disease in the other organism

✔ **Note:** There are organisms that live inside humans in mutualistic relationships. They are nonpathogenic. However, other organisms that enter the body can cause a variety of diseases, generally through the production of toxins that disrupt normal cell functioning.

OBJECTIVE 43	Classes of microorganisms

KEY TERMS

Allergy (al´-uhr-je)—A condition of being highly sensitive to foreign substances that enter the body often because the person's immune system does not respond to the antigen of the substance

Amebic dysentery (uh-me´-bik dis-uhn´-ter-e)—A condition of severe diarrhea often accompanied by blood and mucus that results from an infection of protozoa

Cyst (sist´)—A capsule that forms around microorganisms before they enter dormant periods

✔ **Note:** Some microorganisms enter periods in which they are inactive, often because environment conditions may not be favorable to them, such as during a drought. Cysts are also used to protect the organism as it moves from host to host, especially for parasites that require multiple hosts.

Exoskeleton (ek-so-skel´-uht-uhn)—A characteristic of some organisms in which the outer tissue of parts of the body are hardened to the point that they support attached softer tissues

Giardiasis (je-ar-di´-uh-suhs)—A condition of diarrhea caused by drinking water containing giardia

Host (host´)—The organism that provides the resources required to sustain a parasitic relationship

Infestation (in-fes-ta´-shuhn)—The presence of parasites in the environment, on the skin, or in the hair of a host

Invertebrate (in-vuhrt´-uh-brat)—An organism that does not have an internal skeleton and, specifically, a spinal column

Malaria (muh-ler´-e-uh)—A parasitic infection of red blood cells by plasmodium virus transmitted by the bite of certain species of mosquito

Spore (spor´)—The dormant form of a bacterium or the reproductive form of a fungus

Unicellular (yu-ni-sel´-yuh-luhr)—Consisting of one cell

---

a. Bacterium (bak-tir´-e-uhm)—A widely distributed **unicellular** organism that may or may not cause disease

✔ **Note:** The plural of bacterium is *bacteria.* There are three primary ways of classifying bacteria. They are classified by their shape (see Objective 44), by their arrangements, and by whether they require oxygen (aerobic) or not (anaerobic).

b. Virus (vi´-ruhs)—A subcellular organism that reproduces as a parasite within other organisms and, consequently, is pathogenic

✔ **Note:** Viruses are smaller than bacteria. They consist of DNA or RNA within a protein shell; the protein shell of each virus has a distinct shape. During reproduction, the virus enters a cell in the **host** and uses the chromosomes and enzymes in the cell to replicate itself. The cell will then die. The severity of the disease depends on the kind of cell that is infected. Rabies, chicken pox, measles, influenza, cold sores, polio, and certain tumors are all the result of viruses.

c. Protozoan (prot-uh-zo´-uhn)—A unicellular organism that is adapted for life in water and forms **cysts** that pass from host to host

✔ **Note:** The plural of protozoan is *protozoa.* Many protozoa are pathogenic to humans. Some, such as those that cause **amebic dysentery** and **giardiasis**, are contracted by consuming infected food or water. Others, such as those that cause **malaria**, are spread by other organisms, such as mosquitoes.

d. Fungus (fuhn´-guhs)—A unicellular or multicellular organism that reproduces by means of spores and that may be pathogenic or nonpathogenic

✔ **Note:** The plural of fungus is *fungi.* Many fungi, such as molds and mushrooms, live on dead matter and help to decompose it. Unicellular fungi are called *yeast,* and many of them are pathogenic to humans, causing yeast infections in moist areas of the body, athlete's foot, ringworm, and other conditions. In some cases, persons with weakened immune systems may experience serious illness and even death from inhaling **spores** that infect the pulmonary regions. A yeast-induced illness is called a *mycosis* (mi-ko´-suhs).

e. Worm (wuhrm´)—A multicellular organism that in its parasitic form can be pathogenic to humans

✔ **Note:** Generally referred to as *helminths* (hel´-minths) in the medical profession, parasitic worms can produce very serious **infestations** because they live inside the body and feed on the host's blood and nutrients. Many go through several life stages only some of which are parasitic or that require different hosts for each stage. Flukes, tapeworms, pinworms, and hookworms are examples of helminths that infect humans.

f. Arthropod (ar´-thruh-pawd)—An **invertebrate** organism with six or more jointed legs and an **exoskeleton**

✔ **Note:** All insects, arachnids (such as spiders), and creatures such as lobsters and crabs are arthropods. Some arthropods are parasitic on humans, including ticks, lice, and mites. Many, such as bees, spiders, and scorpions, carry toxins that can be harmful to humans, especially persons with **allergies** to arthropod venom. Arthropods such as ticks, fleas, flies, and mosquitoes can present additional risks to humans by carrying infectious organisms that enter the bloodstream when the arthropod bites.

Classes of microorganisms as classified by their shape

✔ **Note:** One of the means of classifying bacteria and some other unicellular organisms is by their shape. Three of the common microorganism shapes—bacillum (buh-sil′-uhm), coccus (kawk′-uhs), and spirillum (spi-ril′-uhm)—are illustrated in Figures 9 through 11 below. A bacillum is any rod-shaped bacterium; a coccus is any round, spherical, or oval bacterium; and a spirillum is any coiled bacterium.

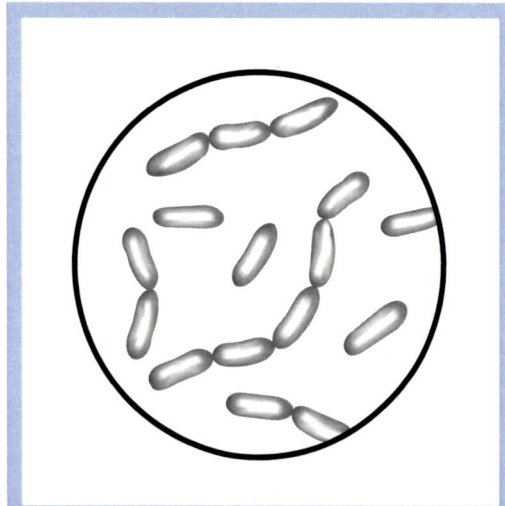

Figure 9
Bacillum

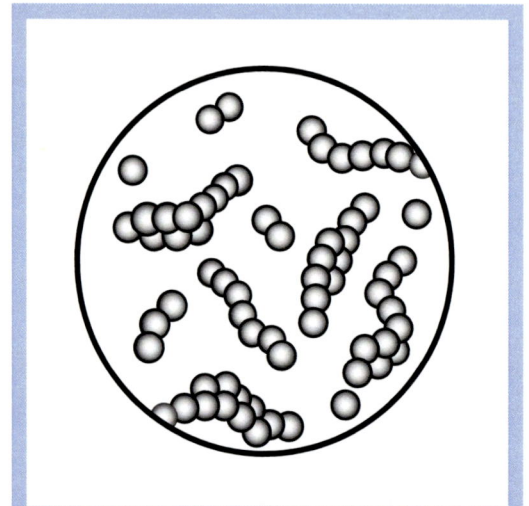

Figure 10
Coccus

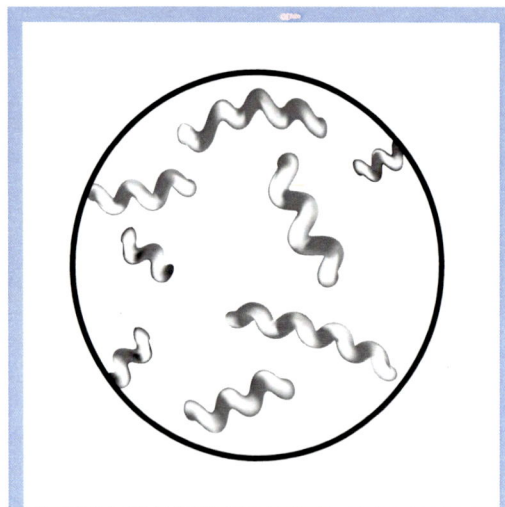

Figure 11
Spirillum

OBJECTIVE 45

The terms *resident flora* and *transient flora*

✔ **Note:** While some organisms are pathogenic to humans, many live in the body or on its surface in mutualistic or commensalistic relationships. These organisms are referred to as *resident flora*. Those organisms that inhabit the body temporarily are referred to as *transient flora*. In some cases, a resident flora will become pathogenic. Typically, this happens when the population of some other resident flora has declined, allowing the organism that becomes pathogenic to multiply well beyond its normal number. An organism that takes advantage of a temporary situation to spread is called an *opportunist*.

a. Resident flora (rez´-uh-dent flor´-uh)—Organisms that normally live in and on the bodies of healthy persons without causing harm when located in specific sites

b. Transient flora (tranz´-e-uhnt flor´-uh)—Organisms that take up residence in or on the body temporarily in a location where they are not normally found

OBJECTIVE 46

Purpose of a gram stain

A gram stain identifies the shape of a pathogen and indicates a positive or negative characteristic of the pathogen that allows preliminary identification of the organism as an aid to diagnosis.

✔ **Note:** The identification and treatment of a disease often depends on interpreting a limited number of clues, such as a person's symptoms. Another clue is the identification of the pathogenic organism involved. One method of identifying bacteria is the gram stain, in which an infected sample, such as saliva, is treated with a dye and examined under a microscope. The shape and color of the organism is apparent under the microscope. Depending on whether the bacteria turn a bluish color or a reddish color, the bacteria can be classed as either gram negative or gram positive. Since a genus will react as either positive or negative and a shape may be particular to a genus or species, the gram-stain test is often enough to specifically identify an organism.

OBJECTIVE 47

Characteristics of bacteria

> KEY TERM
>
> **Facultative** (fak´-uhl-tat-iv)—Having the ability to adapt to more than one condition

a. The tough outer cell wall gives a bacterium its shape.

b. Cocci and bacilli often colonize with each other so that another way of identifying bacteria is by the shape of their colonies.

> ✔ **Note:** The shape of the bacterial groups is added as a prefix to the shape of the organism. Thus, cocci that forms clusters are called *staphylococcus* (staf-uh-lo-kawk´-uhs), those that form chains are called *streptococcus* (strep-tuh-kawk´-uhs), and those that form pairs are called *diplococcus* (dip-lo-kawk´-uhs). There are also strepto- and diplo- forms of bacilli.

c. Bacteria reproduce by binary fission, in which the chromosome duplicates itself and then the cell divides into two identical cells.

d.   Aerobic species require that oxygen be present in order to reproduce.

e.   Anaerobic species require that no oxygen be present in order to reproduce.

f.   **Facultative** anaerobic species can reproduce with or without oxygen.

OBJECTIVE 48

Characteristics of rickettsiae

a.   Rickettsiae (rik-et´-se-uh) are bacteria that can reproduce only within the cells of a living host.

b.   Rickettsiae infect mammals and are often spread by arthropods.

   ✔ **Note:** Two rickettsial diseases include Rocky Mountain spotted fever and typhus, spread by ticks and lice respectively.

c.   Rickettsiae infections can be treated with antibiotics.

OBJECTIVE 49

Characteristics of viruses

a.   Viruses are nucleic acids within shells of protein.

b.   Each virus exhibits a shape that is characteristic of that virus.

c.   Viruses can only reproduce when they are within the living cells of a host organism.

d.   A virus will use the nucleic acid and enzymes of an infected cell to produce other viruses, often multiplying to the point that the host cell ruptures and dies.

e.   The severity of a viral disease depends on the type of cells that are infected.

f.   Some viruses can become dormant so that they present no signs of infection and then become active again after a period of time, even years later.

g.   Some viruses can be transmitted from a pregnant woman to her fetus.

h.   Antiviral medications are difficult to develop because viruses reside inside cells, use the cell's chemicals to reproduce, and offer few functions that can be attacked without harming the host organism.

OBJECTIVE 50

Characteristics of protozoa

a.   Protozoa are unicellular.

b.   Protozoa live in water and soil.

c.   Protozoa can form cysts and become dormant.

d.   Protozoa generally spread from food or water contaminated with cysts.

OBJECTIVE 51	**Characteristics of fungi and algae**

✔ **Note:** Fungi (fuhn´-ji; singular *fungus,* fuhn´-guhs) and algae (al´-je) are two types of plants. They are distinct from each other primarily in that alga has chlorophyll in its cells and can produce its own nourishment in the presence of light. Fungi do not have chlorophyll and must extract their nutrition from an external source, such as decaying organic matter or a live host. Both types of organisms are simple plants and are not differentiated into complex structures such as root systems and leaves. Many types of fungi are capable of infecting humans. Infections with algae are extremely rare with fewer than 100 cases reported in humans.

a. Fungi

- Fungi may be unicellular or multicellular.

- Some fungi are normally found in and on the body.

- Fungi infections may result from the use of antibiotics or reduced resistance due to injuries or diseases.

- Most fungi infections are superficial but can spread to the inside of the body through spores.

b. Algae

- Algae may be unicellular or multicellular.

- Infestation generally occurs as a result of a break in the skin or a trauma, including surgery, and is generally limited to the skin or bursa.

- The most-common symptom is skin lesions that resemble many other conditions so that the diagnosis must be confirmed through laboratory analysis.

OBJECTIVE 52	**Common parasites that afflict humans**

KEY TERM

Vectors (vek´-tuhrs) **of disease**—The conditions that tend to promote the spread of a disease, such as when the bite of an arthropod allows pathogens to enter a person's bloodstream

---

a. Parasitic worms live off nutrients in the host's body, in the host's blood, or on the host itself.

b. Many parasitic worms have several stages of life involving eggs, larvae, and adult stages.

c. Parasitic worms generally inhabit specific body sites.

d. For some species of parasitic worms, the inhabited site varies with the stage of development and may even involve more than one host species.

e. Mites and lice generally afflict the surface of a host's body and present little direct risk to the host.

f. Parasites such as lice, fleas, mosquitoes, and ticks may be **vectors of disease.**

SECTION A:
Introduction to Anatomy and Physiology

Module 3-A: Infection, Immunology, and Sanitation

Module Contents

Page

STUDENT GUIDE
COMPONENTS

STUDENT CD
COMPONENTS

Assignment Sheets

1—Conduct a Sanitation Inspection of the Lab and Classroom

2—Practice Critical Thinking: Complete a Case Study on Immunity and Infection

PREREQUISITE:
Module 2-A

Learning Activities Sheet

Student name _____

DIRECTIONS

Place a checkmark in the appropriate box as you complete each of the steps below.

❏ 1. **Take**   Pretest provided by your instructor.

❏ 2. **Stop**   Have your instructor evaluate your performance. Follow your instructor's recommendations concerning the following learning activities.

❏ 3. **Read**   Module Objective Sheet.

❏ 4. **Study**   Information Sheet, Objectives 1 through 35.

❏ 5. **Research**   Online resources to learn more about infection, immunology, and sanitation. Your instructor will list several Web sites on the blanks below. Visit at least three of the following Web sites.

• _____

• _____

• _____

• _____

• _____

• _____

• _____

❏ 6. **Do**   Assignment Sheet 1, "Conduct a Sanitation Inspection of the Lab and Classroom."

❏ 7. **Stop**   Have your instructor evaluate your performance. If the evaluation is satisfactory, continue to step 8. If the evaluation is not satisfactory, repeat step 6.

❏ 8. **Do**   Assignment Sheet 2, "Practice Critical Thinking: Complete a Case Study on Immunity and Infection."

❏ 9. **Stop**   Have your instructor evaluate your performance. If the evaluation is satisfactory, continue to step 10. If the evaluation is not satisfactory, repeat step 8.

❏ 10. **Take**   Written Test provided by your instructor.

❏ 11. **Stop** Have your instructor evaluate your performance. If the evaluation is satisfactory, continue to step 12. If the evaluation is not satisfactory, repeat step 4.

❏ 12. **Check** With your instructor for any additional assignments to be completed.

❏ 13. **Do** Additional assignments your instructor lists below.

_____

_____

_____

❏ 14. **Take** Module Review provided by your instructor.

❏ 15. **Stop** Have your instructor evaluate your performance. Follow your instructor's recommendations concerning a review of the above learning activities.

❏ 16. **Stop** Have your instructor evaluate your performance on this module by compiling your scores on the Written Test, assignment sheets, and Module Review. If the evaluation is satisfactory, proceed to the next module. If the evaluation is not satisfactory, ask your instructor for further instructions.

Module Objective Sheet

MODULE OBJECTIVE

After completing this module, you should be able to name the sources of the micro-organisms that cause disease, describe the body's defense-mechanism processes, and describe methods used to control the spread of microorganisms. You should demonstrate these competencies by completing the assignment sheets and by scoring a minimum of 85 percent on the Written Test and on the Module Review.

SPECIFIC OBJECTIVES

After completing this module, you should be able to:

1. Define the term *infection*.

2. Complete statements that describe the effects of infection on a human host.

3. Complete statements that describe methods used to reduce the spread of infection.

4. Match types of infections and diseases to their descriptions.

5. Describe the phases in the course of a disease.

6. Complete statements that describe the role of the body's portals of entry and portals of exit in the spread of infectious diseases.

7. List sources of the microorganisms that cause infectious diseases.

8. Select the factors that determine whether a pathogen will cause a disease in a host's body.

9. Describe the factors that influence the virulence of a pathogen in a host's body.

10. Complete statements concerning the functions of the body's physical barriers to infection.

11. Match special structures, chemicals, and actions within the body that provide protection against infection to their functions.

12. Define the term *immunology*.

13. Select true statements concerning types of immunity.

14. Distinguish among the types of cellular and tissue defense-mechanism processes the body uses against disease and infection.

15. Match types of white blood cells to their descriptions.

16. Describe the stages of the interferon response.

17. Complete statements concerning the stages of phagocytosis.

18. Distinguish between the definitions of a T cell and a B cell.

19. Match types of T cells and B cells to their functions.

20. Distinguish between the types of immunity development in the serum-protein response.

21. Select true statements concerning the stages of cell-mediated immunity development in the serum-protein response.

22. Describe the stages of humoral-mediated immunity development in the serum-protein response.

23. Distinguish among the phases of the antibody-production cycle that follows the body's exposure to an antigen.

24. Describe the stages of the inflammatory reaction.

25. Match types of vaccines to their definitions.

26. Define the term *hypersensitive response.*

27. Distinguish among the types of hypersensitive responses.

28. Match methods used to control the spread of microorganisms to their definitions.

29. Explain the reasons certain industries must control the growth of microorganisms.

30. Select true statements concerning the factors that determine the effectiveness of an antimicrobial procedure.

31. Match types of antimicrobial-control methods to their descriptions.

32. List factors that contribute to the spread of nosocomial infections.

33. Match organisms that cause common nosocomial infections to the infections they cause.

34. Select true statements concerning types of patient isolation used in health-care facilities.

35. Complete statements that describe recommended precautions and guidelines used in surgical suites to reduce the spread of infection.

36. Conduct a sanitation inspection of the lab and classroom. (Assignment Sheet 1)

37. Practice critical thinking: complete a case study on immunity and infection. (Assignment Sheet 2)

Information Sheet

OBJECTIVE 1

The term *infection*

KEY TERMS

Disease (diz-ez´)—A specific illness or disorder characterized by a recognizable set of signs and symptoms and attributable to heredity, infection, diet, or environment

Host (host´)—An organism that serves as a permanent or temporary home for another organism

Toxin (tawk´-suhn)—A substance that is harmful to cells

Infection (in-fek´-shuhn)—An invasion of a body by organisms and the reaction of the body to the presence of those organisms and to the **toxins** that they produce; the presence and multiplication of an organism that results in harm or **disease** to a **host**

✔ **Note:** Very small organisms—referred to as *microorganisms* (mi-kro-or´-guh-niz-uhm)—can enter the body during respiration, ingestion, and sexual contact; through wounds; and by other conditions that provide openings into the body (see Objective 6).

OBJECTIVE 2

Effects of infection on a human host

KEY TERMS

Pathogen (path´-uh-juhn)—An organism that is capable of producing disease in another organism

Symptom (sim{p}´-tuhm)—A condition that occurs in association with a disease and that can be evidence of the presence of the disease

Examples: Fever, chills, sluggishness, rash, loss of appetite, watery eyes

a. The harmful effects of an infection on a host may be the direct result of an action taken by a **pathogen** or the result of toxins produced by the pathogen.

   ✔ **Note:** An infecting organism generally causes illness by disrupting the normal activities of a host's cells and, thus, organs.

b. The ability of an infecting organism to harm a host is referred to as *virulence* (vir´-{y} uh-luhns).

   ✔ **Note:** An infecting organism's virulence depends on a number of factors, such as how the organism enters the body, the number of invading pathogens, and other conditions. You will study these factors in Objective 9.

c. The ability of a host to avoid infection and reduce harm caused by an infecting organism is called *resistance* (ri-zis´-tuhns).

✔ **Note:** The resistance of a host depends on a number of factors, such as general health, age, sensitivity to the pathogen, and other factors. You will study thee factors in Objectives 8 and 9.

d. An infection may result in observable **symptoms** in a host, or the infection may occur without symptoms.

e. The period of time between the incidence of infection and the appearance of symptoms in a host is referred to as the *incubation* (in-kyuh-ba´-shuhn) *period.*

f. An infection in a host may be localized, limited to only one organ or site, or it may be systemic, affecting the entire body.

g. The host's body produces special cells that recognize pathogens and destroy them.

✔ **Note:** You will study these cells and their responses in later objectives in this module.

h. Communicable (kuh-myu´-ni-kuh-buhl) diseases are infections that can be spread from one human host to another through direct or indirect contact.

✔ **Note:** You will study ways to prevent the spread of infection in Objective 3 and in later objectives in this module.

OBJECTIVE 3

Methods used to reduce the spread of infection

KEY TERMS

Antibiotic (ant-i-bi-awt´-ik)—A special medication that slows or stops the growth of certain microorganisms

Antiseptic (ant-uh-sep´-tik)—A chemical used to destroy or reduce the growth of pathogens on a person

Disinfectant (dis-uhn-fek´-tuhnt)—A chemical used to destroy or reduce the growth of pathogens on objects

Sterilize (ster´-uh-liz)—To destroy all of the pathogens on an object or in a substance

Vaccination (vak-suh-na´-shuhn)—The administration of a medication that increases the body's resistance to a specific pathogen

---

a. The spread of infection can be reduced by using **antiseptic** practices, cleaning with **disinfectants**, and **sterilizing** instruments and surgical materials.

b. Some infections can be prevented through **vaccinations**.

c. Once an infection has occurred, **antibiotics** can be used to improve the body's ability to fight the infection.

OBJECTIVE 4	**Types of infections and diseases**

a. Localized infection—An infection that involves only one organ or site of a host's body

✔ **Note:** A localized infection may also be referred to as a *local infection.*

b. Systemic infection—An infection that has spread throughout a host's body from an initial site

c. Acute (uh-kyut′) infection—An infection that runs a rapid and severe course and then ends abruptly

Examples: Cold, measles, influenza

d. Chronic (krawn′-ik) infection—An infection that lasts for a long period of time—from weeks to several years

Examples: Advanced tuberculosis, acquired immunodeficiency syndrome (AIDS)

e. Latent (lat′-uhnt) infection—An infection that has no apparent symptoms

Examples: Malaria, early tuberculosis

f. Mixed infection—An infection that results from more than one organism

Examples: Appendicitis, wound infections

g. Nosocomial (nos-uh-ko′-me-uhl) infection—An infection that is contracted in a hospital or other health-care facility, such as a nursing home

✔ **Note:** Caregivers can come into contact with diseases that infect the persons to whom they provide care. The infectious contamination can result from direct contact with the patient or client, through handling their body fluids (blood, urine, stools, saliva, mucus, etc.), or by touching objects that have been contaminated through contact with the patient, including clothing, bedding, bandages, dishes, and such. The caregiver may become infected or may transfer the infection to other caregivers or to patients or clients. Nosocomial infections often result from poor health-care practices.

h. Primary disease—The first-occurring infection within a period of illness

i. Secondary disease—A subsequent infection or complication to an existing condition

✔ **Note:** An illness may lower a person's resistance to fight other infections, allowing other organisms to become established. For example, patients who are confined to a bed for a long period of time are more likely to contract pneumonia, an inflammation of the lungs that may result from infections by microorganisms.

OBJECTIVE 5	**Phases in the course of a disease**

> KEY TERM
> _____
>
> **Convalescence** (kawn-vuh-les´-uhns)—The process of a host's recovery from a disease

a. Incubation—The period of time between the incidence of an infection and the appearance of symptoms in a host

b. Illness—The period of time during which a host exhibits symptoms of a disease

> ✔ **Note:** Some authorities divide the illness phase into two phases called the *prodromal* (pro-dro´-muhl) *phase* and the *acute phase.* The prodromal phase is a short period—usually less than a day—during which time the infection has been established but symptoms are not fully developed. The host may not feel well, but symptoms such as nausea and fever that are to follow are not yet evident. The acute phase is the time during which the symptoms are pronounced.

c. **Convalescence** or death—The resolution of a disease, resulting in a host's recovery or death

> ✔ **Note:** Most illnesses are called *self-limiting*—the body's defenses will overcome the illness in a short time, or the disease is caused by a pathogen that has only a short life cycle within the body. Some illnesses require the use of medications to assure recovery. In some cases, a host does not recover quickly, and some diseases can lead to the host's death. If the disease is not fatal—it does not lead to the host's death—the host may remain afflicted, with the disease becoming chronic. Often chronic illnesses do not lead directly to death, but they may allow secondary infections that can lead to death or that are fatal to the host because of his or her weakened condition from dealing with the chronic condition.

OBJECTIVE 6	**Role of the body's portals of entry and portals of exit in the spread of infectious diseases**

KEY TERMS

Asymptomatic (a-sim{p}-tuh-mat´-ik)—Being without symptoms

Carrier (kar´-e-uhr)—An organism capable of spreading disease

✔ **Note:** A carrier may exhibit symptoms of the disease or may be asymptomatic.

Contagious (kuhn-ta´-juhs)—Communicable, such as a disease that may be transmitted by direct or indirect contact

Genitourinary (jen-uh-to-yur´-uh-ner-e)—Referring to the structures and processes associated with urinary functions and reproduction

Lesion (le´-zhuhn)—A separation in tissue

✔ **Note:** A lesion may be the result of a mechanical injury such as a cut or surgical incision, or it may be the result of an infection that causes the flesh to tear.

Sputum (sp{y}ut´-uhm)—Substance expelled from the respiratory tract that may contain mucus, pus, cellular materials, blood, and other materials

Zoonosis (zo-uh-no´-suhs)—A disease of animals that is transmissible to humans from its primary animal host

Examples: Equine encephalitis, rabies, and yellow fever

✔ **Note:** Infections enter the body through openings called *portals of entry*. A portal of entry may be a natural opening, such as the mouth, or an injury, such as a cut. Infections can be communicated to others through openings called *portals of exit*. For example, when a **contagious** person sneezes, pathogens can exit with the mucus and droplets expelled from the nose.

a. The most-common portals of entry for pathogens are breaks in the skin and natural body openings such as the nose, mouth, and **genitourinary** openings.

b. The most-common portals of exit for pathogens are skin **lesions** and natural body openings such as the nose, mouth, and genitourinary openings.

✔ **Note:** Pathogens are spread by persons coming into contact with the body fluids that leave by means of an infected person's portals of exit. Blood may be transferred from an open wound or by infected needles and instruments. Fecal material and urine can carry pathogens. **Sputum** and saliva carry pathogens from the lungs and mouth. Tears can transmit infections of the eyes. Semen and vaginal secretions can spread pathogens through sexual contact. Breast milk can transmit diseases from a woman to a nursing infant. Other fluids may also contain pathogens that can infect a second person if contact with a portal of entry occurs.

c. Typically, a disease will spread from an infected host's portals of exit to a second host's portals of entry.

d. Hosts who have recovered from a disease or who are **asymptomatic** may be **carriers** and transmit the disease to others.

e. **Zoonosis** is spread to humans from animals.

f. Pathogens that live in the soil, on other surfaces, or in contaminated foods can also enter the body through portals of entry.

OBJECTIVE 7

Sources of the microorganisms that cause infectious diseases

KEY TERMS

Fomite (fo´-mit)—An inanimate object that is contaminated with pathogens and is capable of transmitting pathogens to a human host

Inanimate (in-an´-uh-muht)—Nonliving

---

a. Living hosts

✔ **Note:** Living hosts can transmit a pathogen from itself to another host.

b. **Inanimate** objects or materials

Examples: Transmission of a pathogen by a host's consuming contaminated food or water or contacting **fomites** such as contaminated drinking cups and eating utensils

OBJECTIVE 8

Factors that determine whether a pathogen will cause a disease in a host's body

---

KEY TERMS

Antibody (ant´-i-bawd-e)—A specialized protein produced in the blood plasma in response to bacteria, viruses, or other antigenic substances

✔ **Note:** Antibodies respond to specific structures on the outside of cells that indicate the cell's source. Cells within each host's body are marked as "self" cells by these structures or as antigens (ant´-i-juhns). The antigens of an invasive cell show that it is not part of the self. Upon detecting the antigen of a pathogen, the body will create an antibody that matches the antigen of the invasive organism. The antibody will then bond to the foreign antigen and remove it from the body.

Bacteriocidin (bak-tir´-e-o-si-din)—A medication that kills bacteria

✔ **Note:** While bacteria are a specific type of microorganism, the term *bacteria* is sometimes applied in a general way to any microscopic pathogen.

Phagocyte (fag´-uh-site)—A cell within the body that destroys invading organisms by engulfing and surrounding them

✔ **Note:** Phagocytes often seek out cells to which antibodies have attached.

---

a. Site of the pathogen invasion

✔ **Note:** The portal of entry of the pathogens and the site where the pathogens settle inside the body may determine whether the pathogens will cause illness. Some organisms are only infectious if they enter by a given portal of entry. For example, a host's swallowing the pathogens for malaria will not lead to infection because malarial organisms can only flourish if they enter through the bloodstream. Other organisms must reach a certain site within the body in order to survive.

b. Antibacterial techniques

✔ **Note:** Steps can be taken to reduce the risk of infection through antibacterial techniques. For example, if a person suffers a slight cut while using a knife, the wound should be washed and treated with an antibiotic. The wound may also be dressed—cleaned, medicated, and covered—to protect it and to prevent dirt and other contaminants from entering it.

c. Normal flora

✔ **Note:** The resident flora in and on the surface of our bodies offer some protection against infections because they are likely to be competitors with an invading pathogen. In many cases, the presence of normal flora will prevent the transient organism from becoming established. However, surgery or medications may reduce the population of resident flora, allowing the pathogens to spread, as when yeast infections occur as a result of the administration of antibiotics that reduce the population of resident flora on the skin.

d. **Bacteriocidins**

e. **Antibodies**

f. **Phagocytes**

OBJECTIVE 9   **Factors that influence the virulence of a pathogen in a host's body**

KEY TERMS

Immunity (im-yu´-nuht-e)—The state of being protected from the effects of a pathogen, generally due to having received a vaccination or because of the body's production of antibodies from a previous exposure to the organism

Susceptibility (suh-sep-tuh-bil´-uht-e)—The degree to which a person is likely to contract a disease

a. Ability to infect—The capacity of an organism to cause disease despite a host's resistance

✔ **Note:** Some organisms are generally very effective in their ability to cause an infection despite the host's health and resistance. For example, if a person has not developed **immunity**, exposure to the measles virus will normally result in an 80 to 90 percent infection rate, even among healthy individuals. By contrast, the rhinovirus that causes the common cold is not very effective against persons who are healthy, rested, and well nourished.

b.   Invasiveness (in-va´-siv-nes)—The level of success an organism experiences upon entering a host; a measure of the number of organisms that are able to enter a host's body

✔ **Note:** Invasiveness is tremendously influential in determining whether an infection occurs and how severe it is. Thus, a person who is present when an infected person sneezes across the room will be exposed to the pathogens, but the number of organisms that reach that person will be much lower than those that reach someone standing close to the infected person. If an organism gains entry through the mouth, it may not be as infectious as if it had entered through broken skin.

c.   Toxigenicity (tawk-si-juh-nis´-uht-e)—The relative strength and the amount of toxins produced by an organism

✔ **Note:** The effects of most pathogens come from their disruption of normal cell processes. In most instances, these disruptions are caused by toxins that the pathogen produces, such as enzymes, hemolysis, coagulase, endotoxins, and exotoxins. The pathogen's toxigenicity affects its virulence, especially when considered in terms of the infected person's **susceptibility** to the toxins.

OBJECTIVE 10 **Functions of the body's physical barriers to infection**

KEY TERM

Cerumen (suh-ru´-muhn)—Ear wax, a secretion of the ceruminous glands in the ear canal

---

a.   Perspiration—Helps to cleanse the pores and raise the level of acidity on the skin

b.   Tears—Rid the eyes of contaminants and help to seal and lubricate the eyelids to prevent entry of organisms

c.   Saliva—Contains enzymes that help break down invading pathogens and prevent them from colonizing in the mouth

d.   Vaginal secretions—Maintain a slightly acidic environment to prevent microorganisms from becoming established

e.   Mucus—Provides a coating that prevents pathogens from making direct contact with the skin

f.   **Cerumen**—Provides a coating that prevents pathogens from contacting delicate areas of the skin in the ear canal

g.   Normal flora—Compete with invading microorganisms to prevent them from becoming established

OBJECTIVE 11 | **Functions of the special structures, chemicals, and actions within the body that provide protection against infection**

> KEY TERMS
>
> **Lysozyme** (liˊ-suh-zim)—An enzyme with antiseptic actions that destroys some foreign organisms
>
> **Protective reflex** (pruh-tekˊ-tiv reˊ-fleks)—Coughing, sneezing, vomiting, tearing of the eyes, or other action that provides protection against pathogens

a. Ciliated membranes—Present physical barriers to contaminated particles and help to hold mucus in place

b. **Lysozymes**—Inhibit the growth of bacteria in tears and saliva

c. Digestive fluids—Inhibit the growth of bacteria in the stomach and intestines

d. Normal flora—Compete with invading pathogens

e. Flushing actions—Remove pathogens through the movement of liquids

    Example: Respiration

f. **Protective reflexes**—Generally expel contaminated substances from the body

OBJECTIVE 12 | **The term *immunology***

Immunology—The study of the ways in which the body resists infection

OBJECTIVE 13 | **Types of immunity**

> KEY TERMS
>
> **Immune serum** (im-yunˊ sirˊ-uhm)—A serum that is taken from another organism (animal or human) and that contains antibodies against a specific disease
>
> **Vaccine** (vakˊ-sen)—A suspension of diluted or killed microorganisms administered in order to stimulate the production of antibodies to promote an active immunity to that pathogen
>
> ✔ **Note:** Vaccines may be injected into the bloodstream; however, vaccines that use other portals of entry, such as ingestion, have been developed.

a. Genetic immunity—Immunity based on one's inherited genetic makeup rather than on the production of antibodies

   ✔ **Note:** Essentially, the term *genetic immunity* means that an organism is not susceptible to a given pathogen that may invade it. Genetic immunity may appear in a racial group, within families, or apparently at random in certain individuals. Such immunity may also be species specific—some species of organisms are immune to infection by a pathogen while other species of organisms are susceptible.

b. Naturally acquired active immunity—Long-term immunity acquired when a person contracts a disease and his or her body naturally produces antibodies in response to the pathogen and memory cells that protect that person from the pathogen

✔ **Note:** A naturally acquired active immunity may protect a person from a pathogen for many years or even for the rest of the person's life.

c. Artificially acquired active immunity—Long-term immunity acquired when a person is given a **vaccine** and his or her body produces antibodies in response to the vaccine and memory cells that protect that person from the pathogen

✔ **Note:** Booster vaccinations may be required to provide an individual with lifelong immunity from the pathogen.

d. Naturally acquired passive immunity—Temporary immunity acquired when antibodies are passed to a fetus through the mother's blood or to an infant through the mother's milk when the infant is breast-feeding

e. Artificially acquired passive immunity—Temporary immunity acquired when an **immune serum** is injected into a person's bloodstream

✔ **Note:** An immune serum does not contain memory cells, thus, the immunity provided by the serum is temporary (passive).

OBJECTIVE 14

Types of cellular and tissue defense-mechanism processes the body uses against disease and infection

✔ **Note:** We tend to think of diseases as affecting a person. In truth, the actual invasion that leads to diseases generally occurs at the cell level. There are several ways in which the cell and the body can fight back. First, the cell may release a chemical called *interferon* that interferes with the metabolism of the invading pathogen. The body can fight the infection by activating white blood cells that attack the pathogen individually or in combination with each other. At the tissue level, the body may exhibit an inflammatory reaction that involves physical and chemical responses that make it more difficult for an infection to spread. In this objective, you will learn general definitions for these four defense-mechanism processes. Subsequent objectives cover these defense mechanisms in more detail.

a. Interferon (int-uh-fir´-awn) response—The process by which a cell releases chemicals that interfere with a virus' ability to reproduce within a cell

✔ **Note:** In order to reproduce, viruses must be inside cells. However, the virus cannot multiply and spread if it does not reproduce. While interferon does not prevent the infection of that particular cell, it does prevent the virus from reproducing viruses that could spread to other cells. Artificial interferon is used to fight cancer because of this effect.

b. Phagocytosis (fag-uh-suh-to´-suhs)—The process in which a moving cell engulfs a mass of foreign material

✔ **Note:** Blood consists of three major types of cells: red blood cells, white blood cells, and platelets. These will be discussed in detail in the circulatory-system modules in Module Set II. However, white blood cells play an important role in the body's defense mechanisms and need to be covered here (see Objective 15). For example, one function of certain white blood cells is to clean up dead cells and other debris of metabolism. They perform this function by surrounding the debris through phagocytosis. White blood cells can also perform phagocytosis on invading pathogens as a defense mechanism.

c. Serum-protein response—The process by which components of the blood and lymph analyze captured pathogens to help develop immunity reactions to the pathogens

✔ **Note:** Serum proteins are components of blood and lymph. There are two types of serum-protein responses related to immunity. These are explained further in Objective 20.

d. Inflammatory reaction (inflammatory response)—The process by which tissues in an area of injury or infection work to trap pathogens in the area

✔ **Note:** The interferon response, phagocytosis, and the inflammatory reaction are all intended to provide a defense against a present, immediate pathogen threat. The serum-protein responses provide immediate defense, but they also help to improve the body's immunity as a defense against future invasions of that pathogen (resistance).

OBJECTIVE 15 **Types of white blood cells**

> KEY TERMS
>
> Heparin (hep´-uh-ruhn)—A chemical that helps prevent abnormal blood clotting
> Histamine (his´-tuh-men)—A chemical that makes capillaries more permeable

✔ **Note:** Five types of white blood cells are described below. Each type of white blood cell or leukocyte (lu´-kuh-site) plays a role in one or more of the cell and tissue defense mechanisms. Additionally, for each type of white blood cell, there are variations that serve specific purposes in the body's response to pathogen invasion.

a. Neutrophil (nu´-truh-fil)—A type of white blood cell that is the first to respond to an inflammatory reaction, where it performs phagocytosis on pathogens

✔ **Note:** Neutrophils make up approximately 55 to 70 percent of the white blood cells. Neutrophils provide a quick response that is not as organized and specific as subsequent reactions. Basically, they charge into the infected site and begin attacking foreign materials.

b. Lymphocyte (lim´-fuh-site)—One of two types of white blood cells—a T cell or a B cell—that performs various functions related to recognizing, marking, and remembering pathogens based on their antigens

> ✔ **Note:** Approximately 20 to 35 percent of the white blood cells are lymphocytes. The two major types of lymphocytes—T cells and B cells—are discussed in more detail in Objective 18.

c. Monocyte (mawn´-uh-site)—A type of white blood cell that enlarges to form a macrophage (mak´-ruh-faj) in order to perform more-rapid phagocytosis

> ✔ **Note:** Monocytes compose 3 to 8 percent of all white blood cells. Many specialized macrophages are found throughout the body, where they often are named for the structures with which they are associated. For example, macrophages in the lungs are referred to as *alveolar macrophages,* those in the brain are called *brain microglia,* and those in the liver are *Kupffer cells.* In addition to attacking pathogens, macrophages engulf and dispose of dead and damaged tissue. This function supports the inflammatory response and aids in tissue repair.

d. Eosinophil (e-uh-sin´-uh-fil)—A type of white blood cell that is believed to neutralize toxins such as those secreted by some pathogens

> ✔ **Note:** Eosinophils make up 1 to 3 percent of the body's white blood cells. In their detoxification role, they are also important in dealing with allergic reactions.

e. Basophil (ba´-suh-fil)—A type of white blood cell that, as part of the inflammatory reaction, releases chemicals that allow the capillaries to be penetrated by white blood cells and other substances that accumulate at an infection site

> ✔ **Note:** Basophils represent less than 1 percent of the total number of white blood cells. They contain granules of **heparin** and **histamine**.

OBJECTIVE 16 | **Stages of the interferon response**

KEY TERM
_____

Fibroblast (fib´-ruh-blast)—A flat, elongated cell in the connective tissue

---

a. Invasion—The virus enters the cell.

b. Synthesis—The infected cell produces interferon.

> ✔ **Note:** The presence of the virus stimulates interferon production. Not all cells have the ability to produce interferon, which is simply a protein that cells synthesize. However, **fibroblasts**, which are involved in healing, and many types of leukocytes are especially efficient in interferon production.

c. Release—The infected cell releases interferon into the bloodstream.

> ✔ **Note:** The presence of interferon in the bloodstream may be an additional defense against blood-transported pathogens and may serve as a signal for other defense mechanisms, such as the need for phagocytes.

d. Interference—Interferon chemically attacks the virus and prevents it from multiplying.

✔ **Note:** Viruses are simply unicellular organisms that normally multiply by mitosis. Interferon prevents normal cell division from occurring in the virus. If the virus cannot divide, it will not be able to multiply and spread the infection. Interferon may be largely responsible for the self-limiting nature of many infections.

e. Phagocytosis—The infected cell and the inhabiting virus are engulfed by a phagocyte.

✔ **Note:** Releasing interferon does not save the cell that has been invaded. That cell simply becomes a container for the trapped virus. The cell will die or will be perceived by phagocytes as damaged. The phagocytes will thus engulf and dispose of the cell and the virus.

OBJECTIVE 17 | **Stages of phagocytosis**

KEY TERMS

Lysosome (li´-suh-som)—A particle that contains digestive enzymes and hydrogen peroxide that chemically dissolve an engulfed pathogen

Pseudopod (sud´-uh-pawd)—An extension of the surface of a phagocyte; a "false foot"

---

a. Invagination (in-vaj-uh-na´-shuhn)—A phagocyte folds part of itself to create **pseudopods** that pull a pathogen to the body of the phagocyte.

✔ **Note:** Several pseudopods may form in the surface of the phagocyte. The pseudopods extend toward the material that the phagocyte is going to engulf—the pathogen—wrap around it, and pull the material toward the body of the phagocyte.

b. Engulfment—The pathogen is completely surrounded by the body of the phagocyte.

c. Vacuole formation—The phagocyte creates a vacuole around the engulfed pathogen.

✔ **Note:** The vacuole provides a sac in which the pathogen can be digested. The vacuole is called a *phagosome* (fa´-guh-som) and is moved toward the center of the phagocyte.

d. Fusing—A **lysosome** fuses with the vacuole so that the contents of the lysosome are emptied into the vacuole containing the engulfed pathogen.

e. Release—The phagocyte releases the contents of the vacuole or dies and then eventually decomposes.

✔ **Note:** Phagocytes do not live very long and have essentially served their purpose when they have engulfed and digested invading pathogens or damaged cells and tissue. The accumulation of phagocytes and other debris is the main source of pus in an infection site.

Module 3-A: Infection, Immunology, and Sanitation

The terms *T cell* and *B cell*

> KEY TERM
>
> **Marrow** (mar´-o) — The inner structure of most large bones

a. T cell — Type of lymphocyte that is formed either in the fetal thymus gland or in the bone **marrow** and passes through the thymus on its way to the lymph nodes and spleen

b. B cell — Type of lymphocyte that is formed in fetal bone marrow and moves directly to the lymph nodes and spleen

Types of T cells and B cells and their functions

> KEY TERMS
>
> **Lysis** (li´-suhs) — A process of disintegration or dissolution (as of cells)
> **Sensitized** (sen´-suh-tizd) — Capable of being affected by a specific stimulus

a. Helper T cells — Seek out phagocytes that have engulfed pathogens and examine the antigens of captured pathogens; may also present the foreign antigen to B cells

   ✔ **Note:** Phagocytes present the antigens of a captured pathogen to helper T cells, which become **sensitized** to the pathogen.

b. Sensitized helper T cells — Divide rapidly to produce memory, cytotoxic, and suppressor T cells

c. Memory T cells — Carry the imprint of a particular pathogen's antigens and store the imprint in preparation for future invasions of the pathogen

d. Cytotoxic (sit-uh-tawk´-sik) T cells — Chemically rupture the cell membrane of infected cells to prevent the pathogen from reproducing and also produce chemicals called *cytokines* (si´-to-kins) that attract phagocytes to the area where the pathogen is located

   ✔ **Note:** Cytotoxic T cells are also referred to as *killer T cells.* The rupturing of the pathogen's cell membrane is referred to as *lysis.*

e. Suppressor T cells — Suppress the immune response once a foreign antigen has been destroyed

f. Inactive B cells — Reside in the liver, spleen, and lymph nodes until exposed to the antigen of their target pathogen

g. Activated B cells — Divide into memory B cells and plasma cells

h. Memory B cells — Remember the antigen and will become involved in responding to any subsequent invasion by that pathogen

i. Plasma cells — Produce antibodies specific to a pathogen's antigen and tag the pathogen cells for destruction by phagocytes

OBJECTIVE 20 | **Types of immunity development in the serum-protein response**

> KEY TERM
>
> _____
>
> Humoral (hum´-uh-ruhl)—Referring to the old concept of the body having four basic humors or fluids, including the plasma in which humoral-immunity development takes place

✔ **Note:** As noted previously, immunity depends on the ability of the body's defense mechanisms to recognize invading pathogens. Such recognition may be nonspecific, such as when a phagocyte attacks any cell that it does not recognize as "self." On the other hand, immunity may be specific to a pathogen due to the body's ability to recognize the antigens of that pathogen. The body uses two processes to acquire this type of immunity as described in this objective.

    a.   Cell-mediated immunity—Relies on the ability of memory T cells to recognize a pathogen's antigen

    b.   Humoral-mediated immunity—Relies on the production of antibodies that will recognize subsequent invasions of a pathogen

        ✔ **Note:** Because of the involvement of antibodies, this process is also referred to as *antibody-mediated immunity.*

OBJECTIVE 21 | **Stages of cell-mediated immunity development in the serum-protein response**

    a.   Phagocyte location—T cells are released in a form called helper T cells to seek out phagocytes that have engulfed pathogens.

    b.   Sensitization—The T cells become sensitized to the pathogen antigens in the phagocytes.

    c.   Cloning—The sensitized helper T cells form other sensitized helper cells and memory, cytotoxic, and suppressor T cells.

    d.   Pathogen binding—The cloned cells travel to the site of the infection and attach to the antigen of pathogen cells.

    e.   Cytokine release—The cytotoxic T cells secrete cytokines to disrupt pathogen metabolism and to attract phagocytes to the area.

    f.   Macrophage response—Macrophages migrate to the infection site and engulf pathogens and damaged cells.

    g.   Suppression—Suppressor T cells secrete macrophage-inhibiting chemicals once the foreign antigen has been destroyed.

Module 3-A: Infection, Immunology, and Sanitation

<table>
<tr><td>OBJECTIVE 22</td><td>**Stages of humoral-mediated immunity development in the serum-protein response**</td></tr>
</table>

Stages of humoral-mediated immunity development in the serum-protein response

a. Sensitization—Helper T cells present the pathogen antigen to B cells, which become sensitized to the antigen.

b. Cloning—The B cells form memory B cells and plasma cells.

c. Antibody production—The plasma cells produce antibodies specific to the pathogen's antigen and tag the pathogen cells for destruction by phagocytes.

d. Macrophage response—Macrophages migrate to the infection site and engulf pathogens and damaged cells.

e. Complement cascade—Enzymes in the plasma cause a chain of chemical reactions that result in the complement components rupturing pathogen cells and in other actions such as attracting neutrophils to the site.

✔ **Note:** The plasma complement includes around 20 proteins that work together when activated to respond to a pathogen invasion. In some cases, the complement response can take place for nonspecific immunity without involving antibodies.

OBJECTIVE 23

Phases of the antibody-production cycle that follows the body's exposure to an antigen

✔ **Note:** The following cycle occurs whether the initial infection occurs naturally or as a result of a vaccination.

a. Lag phase—The phase during which the body detects an unrecognized foreign antigen and begins to react

✔ **Note:** Generally, the body produces antibodies only after an exposure to an unrecognized foreign antigen. The body recognizes its own antigens and usually only attacks foreign antigens.

b. Primary-response phase—The phase during which the body produces (1) antibodies that "fit" the previously unrecognized antigen and (2) memory cells that will recognize that antigen during any subsequent exposure

✔ **Note:** The number of antibodies produced during the primary-response phase is generally not enough to prevent an infection, so the person usually becomes sick. After the invading antigens are removed from the body following an illness, the number of antibodies in the bloodstream declines, but the memory cells remain.

c. Secondary-response phase—The phase during which the body is exposed to a subsequent invasion by an antigen, the memory cells immediately recognize the antigen, and the body produces antibodies against it

✔ **Note:** If there is a second invasion by a foreign antigen, the body immediately recognizes the antigen and begins to produce antibodies based on the "memory" of the first infection. Consequently, in many cases, the body is able to produce enough antibodies in a short enough time to prevent the antigen from becoming established, and the person may not become sick.

OBJECTIVE 24

Stages of the inflammatory reaction

KEY TERMS

Constrict (kuhn-strikt´)—To grow smaller or narrower

Dilate (di-lat´)—To grow larger or expand

✔ **Note:** The terms *dilate* and *constrict* have opposite meanings. Both terms are used often in anatomy and physiology. Blood vessels constrict and dilate, and so do the pupils of the eyes, as well as other body structures.

Exudate (ek´-shu-dat)—A substance that has oozed from a body, such as from a cell

✔ **Note:** As you learned in Objective 14, the inflammatory reaction is a set of responses made by the body at the site of an injury or infection to trap pathogens in a localized area. Inflammation and the inflammatory reaction are also discussed in Module 4 of this module set. This objective concentrates on the infection-fighting aspects of the inflammatory reaction.

a. Constriction—The blood vessels **constrict** to allow blood to pool at the affected site.

b. Dilation—The blood vessels **dilate**, and white blood cells gather in the affected site to fight infection.

c. Exudation—The injured or infected cells secrete **exudate** that causes the area to swell.

d. Barrier formation—The exudate creates a fibrous network that prevents pathogens from spreading from the area.

OBJECTIVE 25

Types of vaccines

KEY TERMS

Attenuated (uh-ten´-yuh-wat-uhd)—Weakened or lessened in power or effect

Toxoid (tawk´-soid)—A toxin that has been modified so as not to be harmful

✔ **Note:** Vaccines are intended to provide protection against a specific pathogen. To produce the vaccine, an organism must serve as a source of antigens so that the body will make antibodies in response to the vaccination. The source organism may be the actual pathogen or one that is closely enough related to the target pathogen that the resulting vaccine will produce an antibody response in the vaccinated organism. The pathogen or related species may be living or killed, or a portion of the pathogen, such as bacterial capsules or toxins, may be used.

a. Nonpathogenic strain—A vaccine that contains organisms of the same genus as the target pathogen but that are a species of subspecies that is not pathogenic

Example: Some influenza vaccines

b. Closely related microorganism—A vaccine that contains nonpathogenic organisms that are chemically similar to the target pathogen

Example: Early small-pox vaccinations that were based on the pathogen for cow pox

c. **Attenuated** living pathogen—A vaccine that contains live weakened or less-virulent forms of the target pathogen

Examples: Live oral polio vaccine, live attenuated measles vaccine

d. Killed pathogen—A vaccine that contains nonliving or inactivated pathogens

Examples: Vaccine for rabies, vaccine for typhoid fever

e. Extract of pathogen—A vaccine that contains components of the pathogen, such as bacterial capsules

Examples: Pneumococcal polysaccharide vaccine, *Haemophilus b* conjugate vaccine

f. **Toxoid**—A vaccine that contains toxins or toxoids of the pathogen

Examples: Vaccine for diphtheria, vaccine for tetanus

OBJECTIVE 26

The term *hypersensitive response*

Hypersensitive (hi-puhr-sen´-suht-iv) **response**—An excessive response by the body's immune system to a foreign substance

✔ **Note:** In some individuals, the hypersensitive response is so excessive that the body may disrupt normal cell functions to attack the foreign substance, even to lowering blood pressure to a fatal level in a condition called *anaphylactic shock* (an-uh-fuh-lak´-tik shawk´). Hypersensitive responses to relatively harmless substances—pollen, peanuts, insect venom, etc.—are called *allergic reactions* (uh-luhr´-jik re-ak´-shuhns), and the precipitating stimulus is referred to as an *allergen* (al´-uhr-juhn).

OBJECTIVE 27

Types of hypersensitive responses

KEY TERM

Congenital (kawn-jen´-uh-tuhl)—Present at birth as a result of conditions in the womb

a. Immediate—Hypersensitive response upon exposure to an allergen and due to an antigen/antibody reaction

b. Delayed—Hypersensitive response following exposure to an allergen and due to body cells reacting to the allergen

c. Autoimmunity—Hypersensitive response to one's own antigens

✔ **Note:** Autoimmune disorders can be caused by a number of conditions and can lead to a number of illnesses, such as some forms of diabetes, arthritis, and multiple sclerosis.

d. Isoimmunity—Hypersensitive response to antigens from one's own species

✔ **Note:** Isoimmunity is one of the principal reasons why a person's body rejects a transplanted organ or tissue and why a pregnant woman's body sometimes creates antibodies that attack the antigens of her fetus, resulting in birth defects or congenital diseases in the fetus.

OBJECTIVE 28

Methods used to control the spread of microorganisms

a. Antiseptic (ant-uh-sep´-tik)—A chemical used to destroy or reduce the growth of pathogens on people

b. Disinfectant (dis-uhn-fek´-tuhnt)—A chemical used to destroy or reduce the growth of pathogens on objects

c. Broad-spectrum antibiotic (brawd´ spek´-truhm ant-i-bi-awt´-ik)—A chemical used to treat bacterial infections that may be caused by a wide variety of bacteria

d. Narrow-spectrum antibiotic (nar´-o spek´-truhm ant-i-bi-awt´-ik)—A chemical used to treat infections caused by a specific kind of bacterium or a few kinds of bacteria

e. Sterilization (ster-uh-luh-za´-shuhn)—A process that destroys pathogens on surfaces

f. Pasteurization (pas-chuh-ruh-za´-shuhn)—A process of heating a food to destroy pathogens in the food

Example: Pasteurization of milk

OBJECTIVE 29

Reasons certain industries must control the growth of microorganisms

a. Public health—To prevent the spread of illness

b. Food preservation—To keep microorganisms from destroying food and to prevent the spread of disease through infected food

c. Production of sterile products—To prevent contamination of the products during the production process

d. Research—To produce pathogens under controlled circumstances to gain better understanding of them and to develop vaccines and other control measures for them

OBJECTIVE 30 | **Factors that determine the effectiveness of an antimicrobial procedure**

a. Immediacy of initial treatment—The effectiveness of an antimicrobial procedure depends on how quickly the antimicrobial procedure was performed after the possibility of a microbial invasion.

b. Interval between treatments—The effectiveness of an antimicrobial procedure depends on how much time has passed between the initial antimicrobial procedure and a subsequent procedure.

✔ **Note:** Timing of treatments has a tremendous impact on the effectiveness of an antimicrobial procedure. Basically, such treatments are a race against the growth rate of the pathogen. If the initial treatment is delayed, the pathogen will have multiplied and gotten a head start over the effectiveness of the procedure. Similarly, if there are delays between treatments, those pathogens that survive an initial treatment will have time to multiply before the procedure is repeated.

c. High temperature—The effectiveness of an antimicrobial procedure is increased if the procedure is performed under extremely high temperatures.

d. Low temperature—The effectiveness of an antimicrobial procedure can be increased if the procedure is performed under extremely low temperatures.

✔ **Note:** Extremely high temperatures and, in some cases, extremely low temperatures can kill microbes; however, warm temperatures can actually promote the spread of microorganisms.

e. Concentration—The strength of the antimicrobial substance used in an antimicrobial procedure can increase the effectiveness of the procedure.

f. Type of microbe—The effectiveness of an antimicrobial procedure is increased when the proper procedure is selected for the type of microbe it will be used against.

g. Number of microbes—The effectiveness of an antimicrobial procedure is increased if the procedure is initiated before there are a great number of microbes to be killed.

h. Microbial defense—The effectiveness of an antimicrobial procedure is increased if the microbe has not been overly exposed to the procedure and has developed defenses against the procedure.

OBJECTIVE 31 | **Types of antimicrobial-control methods**

✔ **Note:** Physical methods are those techniques that kill or remove pathogens using physical barriers or energy transported by various means. There is not a chemical reaction or poisoning of the pathogen.

Physical methods

a. Barrier—Physical method used to prevent microbes from reaching portals of entry

Examples: Gloves, face shield

b.   Moist heat—Physical method used to kill microbes through the combined effect of heat and water that is at a temperature short of boiling

c.   Dry heat—Physical method used to kill microbes through the effects of heat from a source such as an oven or an infrared light

d.   Pressurized steam—Physical method used to kill all microbes and their spores through the effects of an autoclave

e.   Cold—Physical method that will not generally kill microbes but is used to slow their growth

f.   Drying—Physical method used to reduce the growth of fungi and some bacteria

g.   Radiation—Physical method used to kill microbes on materials such as plastics that cannot be subjected to high temperatures

h.   Ultrasonic waves—Physical method used to kill microbes on materials that can be safely exposed to microwaves

i.   Filtration—Physical method used to control microbes in a fluid (liquid or gas) by forcing the fluid through a material with openings that allow the fluid to pass through but are too small to allow pathogens to pass through, leaving pathogens trapped in the material

Chemical methods

✔ **Note:** Chemical control of microbes is generally achieved by lysis, damaging the pathogen's genetic material, or interfering with its metabolism, as by inactivating enzymes within the pathogen.

a.   Antiseptic—Chemical method used to destroy bacteria on living organisms

b.   Disinfectant—Chemical method used to destroy bacteria on inanimate objects

c.   Sterilant—Chemical method used to destroy all organisms on inanimate objects

OBJECTIVE 32   **Factors that contribute to the spread of nosocomial infections**

a.   Improper hand-washing techniques

b.   Inappropriate use of antibiotics

✔ **Note:** Excessive use of antibiotics can cause the pathogens to become resistant to the effects of the medication. Antibiotics can also destroy resident flora, allowing other organisms to gain a competitive advantage.

c.   False sense of security

✔ **Note:** Patients and caregivers are both likely to assume that the hospital and routine care techniques as well as the treatment being given are a means of protecting the patient from infections.

d. Type of surgery performed on patient

> ✔ **Note:** Some types of surgeries are more likely to lead to infections than others. Surgeries involving the abdomen, especially the intestines, may expose other parts of the body to resident microbes that are normally nonpathogenic. Burns and other injuries that break the surface of the skin and make it difficult to close off portals of entry are more likely to become infected.

e. Caregiver's patient load

> ✔ **Note:** When caregivers have frequent contact with a number of patients, their risk of exposure is increased.

f. Type of care procedure performed

> ✔ **Note:** Procedures that require the handling of body fluids, soiled dressings and bedding, exposure of surgical incisions, and close contact with contagious patients increase the risk of nosocomial infections.

g. Facility staffing

> ✔ **Note:** The number of staff members, the quality of their training, how conscientious they are, and other personal factors can contribute to the spread of infections in a health-care facility.

h. Administration of an immunosuppressive agent

> ✔ **Note:** Immunosuppressive (im-yu-no-suh-pres´-iv) agents are given to patients who have had organ or tissue transplants to reduce the chances that the patient's immune system will attack the foreign cells. Persons receiving these agents are more likely to contract other infections because of their reduced defense mechanisms.

OBJECTIVE 33

Organisms that cause common nosocomial infections and the infections they cause

---

KEY TERM

Colitis (ko-lit´-uhs)—An inflammatory condition of the large intestine characterized by severe diarrhea, bleeding, and ulceration of the mucosa of the intestine

---

a. Staphylococcus aureus (staf-uh-lo-kawk´-uhs or´-e-uhs)—Responsible for a number of post-operative infections commonly referred to as *staph infections*

b. Streptococcus (strep-tuh-kawk´-uhs) species—Involved in "strep" throat, scarlet fever, pneumonia, rheumatic heart disease, and other communicable conditions

c. Esherichia coli (esh-er-ik´-i-uh ko´-li)—Responsible for various infections referred to as *colitis*

> ✔ **Note:** *E. coli* normally reside in the human intestinal tract with no ill effect; however, during surgical procedures, the microbes may be spread to other parts of the body where they can cause various infections. *E. coli* is one of the most-common sources of nosocomial infections.

d. Pseudomonas aeruginosa (sud-uh-mo´-nuhs uh-rug´-i-no-suh)—Presents a particular hazard for various infections to burn victims, patients with cystic fibrosis, and those patients with certain types of cancer where the skin and mucous membranes do not afford adequate protection

> ✔ **Note:** *Pseudomonas aeruginosa* normally inhabits soil and water and is a transient flora for the intestines.

e. Mycobacterium (mi-ko-bak-tir´-e-uhm) species—Responsible for tuberculosis and leprosy and present a particular hazard for various infections to patients with low resistance, such as those with acquired immunodeficiency syndrome (AIDS), to those receiving immunosuppressors, and to those with pulmonary conditions

> ✔ **Note:** Some mycobacterium species are found in the lungs with no ill effects on the host.

f. Human immunodeficiency virus (HIV)—Responsible for AIDS

> ✔ **Note:** HIV is of particular concern to health-care workers because it can be spread through body fluids.

g. Hepatitis (hep-uh-tit´-uhs) B virus—Responsible for hepatitis

> ✔ **Note:** Hepatitis B virus is one of three common strains, though other strains exist. Hepatitis B is a significant threat in health care because it can be spread through body fluids.

h. Human papilloma (hu´-muhn pap-uh-lo´-muh) virus—Associated with several types of cancer, including cancers of the mouth and cervix

OBJECTIVE 34

Types of patient isolation used in health-care facilities

> KEY TERM
>
> ---
>
> Enteric (en-ter´-ik)—Pertaining to the intestine
> ✔ **Note:** Enteric pathogens are present in feces and other alimentary-system wastes and can be spread in that way.

✔ **Note:** Over time, there have been many modifications to the recommended methods of patient isolation. The Hospital Infection Control Practices Advisory Committee (HICPAC) of the Centers for Disease Control recommends such guidelines. At the time of this writing, HICPAC recommended three types of transmission-based precautions for airborne, droplet, and contact transmissions of infections. These special precautions are to be modified by hospitals for local use. The list below gives some common types of isolation that have been used over the years and some general guidelines. Health-care workers are responsible for knowing the specific requirements for their facilities. More information with regard to these practices is available on the National Institute of Health web site at http://www.nih.gov.

a. Total—Isolation that requires a patient to have no contact with anyone

✔ **Note:** Total isolation is also referred to as *strict isolation*.

b. Protective—Isolation that requires that a patient not be exposed to infection risks

c. **Enteric**—Isolation that requires protection with regard to a patient's intake and output of food and liquids

d. Wound and skin—Isolation that requires the use of barriers to prevent contact with moist areas

✔ **Note:** Wound and skin isolation may also be called *drainage/secretion precautions*.

e. Respiratory—Isolation that requires the use of a mask and separation of a patient from contact with other patients

✔ **Note:** Other special requirements may be necessary for patients with tuberculosis.

f. Blood/body fluids—Isolation that requires the use of gloves and other barriers and proper disposal of body fluids and contaminated materials

✔ **Note:** This type of isolation is sometimes referred to as *body-substance isolation*.

OBJECTIVE 35

Recommended precautions and guidelines used in surgical suites to reduce the spread of infection

---

KEY TERMS

No-touch passing—Passing an object so that neither the person handing nor the person taking the object touches the object near a cutting edge

Sharps (sharps´)—Instruments such as scalpels, needles, tweezers, and other devices that are capable of separating flesh; also includes foreign bodies such as glass, metal fragments, splinters, knives, and other objects that may be removed from the body and then present hazards to health-care workers

Venipuncture (ven´-uh-puhn{k}-chuhr)—A procedure that involves puncturing a vein

---

✔ **Note:** Each facility will have its own set of procedures for reducing the spread of infection. The following guidelines are based on the standard precautions that the Centers for Disease Control (CDC) recommend whenever there is a chance of exposure to body-fluid-borne pathogens, including the human immunodeficiency virus (HIV).

a. Hands and other skin surfaces should be washed immediately and thoroughly if contaminated with blood or other body fluids.

b. Handling of body fluids and specimens should only be done while wearing goggles, masks, gloves, and impermeable clothing.

✔ **Note:** The CDC recommends: "all health-care workers should routinely use appropriate barrier precautions to prevent skin and mucous-membrane exposure when contact with blood or other body fluids of any patient is anticipated. Gloves should be worn for touching blood and body fluids, mucous membranes, or non-intact skin of all patients, for handling items or surfaces soiled with blood or body fluids, and for performing **venipuncture** and other vascular-access procedures. Gloves should be changed after contact with each patient."

c. Hands should be washed immediately after gloves are removed.

d. Used **sharps** should be placed in disposable containers, using **no-touch passing**.

e. Used needles should not be recapped.

> ✔ **Note:** The CDC recommends: "all health-care workers should take precautions to prevent injuries caused by needles, scalpels, and other sharp instruments or devices during procedures; when cleaning used instruments; during disposal of used needles; and when handling sharp instruments after procedures. To prevent needlestick injuries, needles should not be recapped, purposely bent or broken by hand, removed from disposable syringes, or otherwise manipulated by hand."

f. Staples should be used instead of sutures whenever possible.

> ✔ **Note:** Staples present lower risk of accidental pricking of medical-staff members than does the use of a needle to sew sutures.

g. After they are used, disposable syringes and needles, scalpel blades, and other sharp items should be placed in puncture-resistant containers for disposal.

h. Reusable instruments and equipment should be subjected to a level of sterilization that will ensure terminal exposure for pathogens.

i. Health-care workers who have sores or skin conditions that exude fluids should refrain from all direct patient care and from handling patient-care equipment until the condition resolves.

> ✔ **Note:** The CDC advises: "pregnant health-care workers are not known to be at greater risk of contracting HIV infection than health-care workers who are not pregnant; however, if a health-care worker develops HIV infection during pregnancy, the infant is at risk of infection resulting from perinatal transmission. Because of this risk, pregnant health-care workers should be especially familiar with and strictly adhere to precautions to minimize the risk of HIV transmission."

SECTION A:
Introduction to Anatomy and Physiology

Module 4-A: Tissues, Membranes, and Wound Healing

Module Contents

PREREQUISITE:
Module 3-A

Learning Activities Sheet

Student name _____

DIRECTIONS

Place a checkmark in the appropriate box as you complete each of the steps below.

❏ 1. **Take** Pretest provided by your instructor.

❏ 2. **Stop** Have your instructor evaluate your performance. Follow your instructor's recommendations concerning the following learning activities.

❏ 3. **Read** Module Objective Sheet.

❏ 4. **Study** Information Sheet, Objectives 1 through 13.

❏ 5. **Research** Online resources to learn more about tissues, membranes, and wound healing. Your instructor will list several Web sites on the blanks below. Visit at least three of the following Internet sites.

- _____
- _____
- _____
- _____
- _____
- _____
- _____

❏ 6. **Do** Assignment Sheet 1, "Develop a Presentation on Basic Tissue of the Human Body."

❏ 7. **Stop** Have your instructor evaluate your performance. If the evaluation is satisfactory, continue to step 8. If the evaluation is not satisfactory, repeat step 6.

❏ 8. **Study** Information Sheet, Objectives 14 through 30.

❏ 9. **Do** Assignment Sheet 2, "Practice Critical Thinking: Complete Case Studies That Consider How Tissues and Membranes Function to Maintain the Body as a Whole."

❏ 10. **Stop** Have your instructor evaluate your performance. If the evaluation is satisfactory, continue to step 11. If the evaluation is not satisfactory, repeat steps 8 and 9.

❏ 11. **Take**   Written Test provided by your instructor.

❏ 12. **Stop**   Have your instructor evaluate your performance. If the evaluation is satisfactory, continue to step 13. If the evaluation is not satisfactory, repeat steps 4 and 8.

❏ 13. **Check**   With your instructor for any additional assignments to be completed.

❏ 14. **Do**   Additional assignments your instructor lists below.

_____

_____

_____

❏ 15. **Take**   Module Review provided by your instructor.

❏ 16. **Stop**   Have your instructor evaluate your performance. Follow your instructor's recommendations concerning a review of the above learning activities.

❏ 17. **Stop**   Have your instructor evaluate your performance on this module by compiling your scores on the Written Test, assignment sheet, and Module Review. If the evaluation is satisfactory, proceed to the next module. If the evaluation is not satisfactory, ask your instructor for further instructions.

Module Objective Sheet

MODULE OBJECTIVE

After completing this module, you should be able to describe types of tissues and membranes, abnormalities in organ tissues and membranes, and the body's wound-healing process. You should demonstrate these competencies by completing the assignment sheets and by scoring a minimum of 85 percent on the Written Test and on the Module Review.

SPECIFIC OBJECTIVES

After completing this module, you should be able to:

1. Define the term *tissue.*

2. Match the basic types of tissue to their descriptions.

3. State the functions of the basic types of tissue.

4. Complete statements that describe the characteristics of the epithelium.

5. Describe the types of epithelial tissue as classified by shape.

6. Define the types of epithelial tissue as classified by tissue-layer arrangement.

7. Match the classes of epithelial tissue to their functions.

8. Match the types of connective tissue to their functions.

9. Define the basic types of nerve tissue.

10. State the functions of the basic parts of a neuron.

11. Complete statements that describe how neurons function in the nervous system.

12. Select true statements concerning the functions of the four types of neuroglia.

13. Describe the factors that determine muscle-tissue classifications.

14. Match types of muscle contractions to their definitions.

15. Define the term *neuromuscular excitability.*

16. Complete statements that describe the neuromuscular-excitability response.

17. Distinguish among the main types of membranes.

18. Select true statements concerning the functions of the main types of membranes.

19. Define the term *organ.*

20. List the types of tissues and membranes found in selected organs.

21. Complete statements that describe how organ systems function.

22. Match terms that describe abnormalities in organ development to their definitions.

23. Select true statements concerning the types of injuries that can damage tissue.

24. Match the types of traumatic wounds to their definitions.

25. Distinguish among the characteristics of the inflammation response.

26. Complete statements that describe the phases in the body's healing response.

27. Distinguish among statements that describe the types of treatment responses in the treatment of wounds.

28. Select true statements concerning the factors that affect the wound-healing process.

29. Complete statements that describe the factors that present possible complications to the wound-healing process.

30. Match the classifications of surgical wounds to their descriptions.

31. Develop a presentation on basic tissue of the human body. (Assignment Sheet 1)

32. Practice critical thinking: complete case studies that consider how tissues and membranes function to maintain the body as a whole. (Assignment Sheet 2)

Information Sheet

OBJECTIVE 1 | **The term *tissue***

Tissue—A collection of cells that share a similar structure and are organized to perform a specific function

OBJECTIVE 2 | **Basic types of tissue**

KEY TERM

Epithelium (ep-uh-the´-le-uhm)—The covering of the internal organs of the body, also the lining of the vessels, body cavities, glands, and organs

---

   a.   Epithelial (ep-uh-the´-le-uhl) tissue—Tissue consisting of cells bound by connective material and varying in the number of layers and in the kinds of cells

        ✔ **Note:** Epithelial tissue forms the **epithelium**. The epithelium in different parts of the body is made of simple squamous cells, simple cuboidal cells, and stratified columnar cells. For example, the stratified squamous epithelium of the epidermis comprises five different cellular layers. Objectives 4 through 7 discuss the epithelial tissue and its functions.

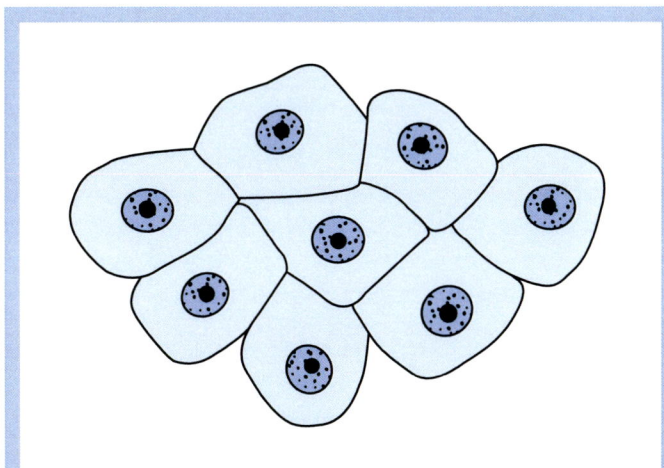

Figure 1
Epithelial tissue (surface view)

b. Connective (kuh-nek´-tiv) tissue—Dense tissue containing large numbers of cells and large amounts of intercellular material composed of fibers in a matrix or ground substance that may be liquid, gelatinous, or solid

✔ **Note:** The ten kinds of connective tissue are discussed in Objective 8. Fibrous tissue is one of those types and is shown in Figure 2.

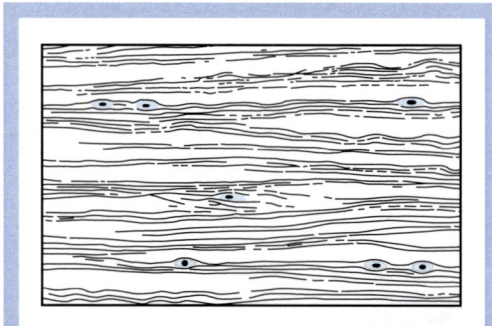

Figure 2
Connective tissue (fibrous tissue)

c. Nerve (nuhrv´) tissue—Tissue consisting of one or more bundles of impulse-carrying fibers that connect the brain and the spinal cord with other parts of the body

✔ **Note:** Objectives 9 through 12 discuss the types of nerve tissue and their functions. Figure 3 shows a type of nerve tissue called a *neuron*.

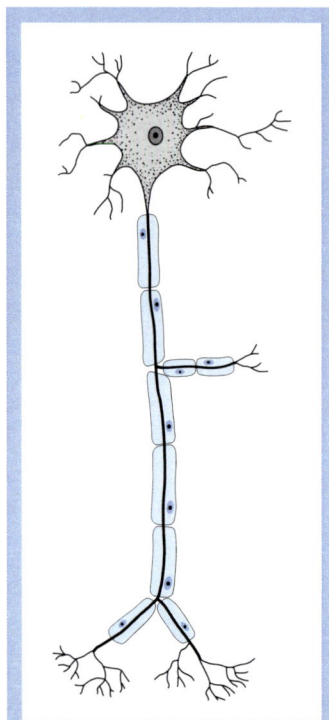

Figure 3
Nerve tissue (neuron)

d. Muscle (muhs´-uhl) tissue—Tissue composed of fibers that are able to contract, causing and allowing movement of the parts and organs of the body

✔ **Note:** Objective 13 discusses the classifications of muscle tissue. Figure 4 shows skeletal muscle tissue.

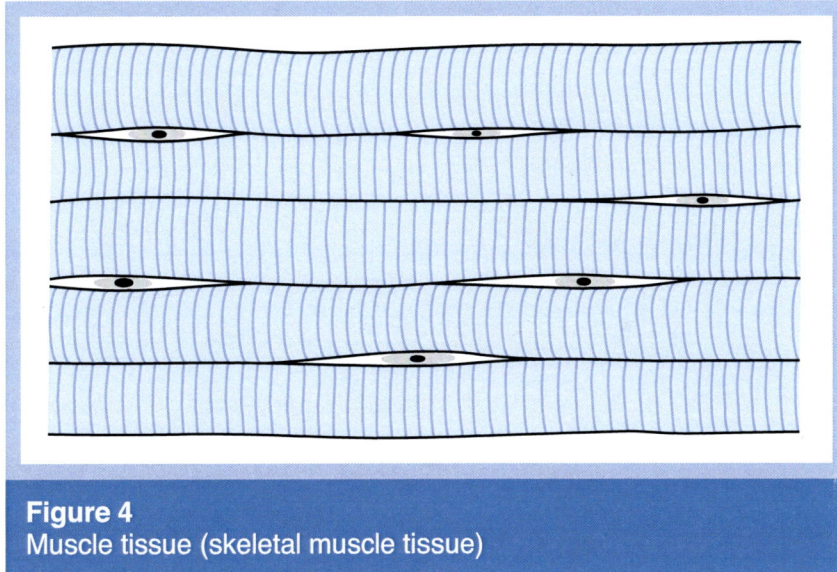

Figure 4
Muscle tissue (skeletal muscle tissue)

OBJECTIVE 3   **Functions of the basic types of tissue**

a. Epithelial tissue—Provides a protective barrier against extreme temperatures, environmental contaminants, and invasions by microorganisms while allowing secretion and excretion of wastes

b. Connective tissue—Binds to other tissue structures to support and organize the body; binds to foreign cells to protect the body; binds to molecules to transport materials through the body

c. Nerve tissue—Conducts electrical signals through the body

d. Muscle tissue—Allows the movement of the movable structures of the body

OBJECTIVE 4 | **Characteristics of the epithelium**

KEY TERMS

Basement membrane—The fragile, noncellular layer of tissue that secures the overlying layers of stratified epithelium

Diffusion (dif-yu´-zhuhn)—The process of a substance moving from an area of high concentration to an area of lower concentration

Membrane (mem´-bran)—A thin layer of tissue that covers a surface, lines a cavity, or divides a space

Serous (sir´-uhs)—Epithelial tissue that lines closed body cavities and covers the organs in that cavity

a. The epithelium covers the body and many of its parts.

b. The epithelium lines the body's **serous** cavities; blood and lymph vessels; and the respiratory, digestive, and urinary tracts.

c. The body's glands consist of epithelial tissue.

d. Cells that compose the epithelium are compactly arranged with little intercellular substance.

e. The epithelium always rests on a layer of connective tissue with a **basement membrane** between them.

f. There are no capillaries within the epithelium, which means that oxygen and nutrients must be provided by the underlying connective tissue through **diffusion**.

g. Epithelial cells undergo constant mitosis in order to replace the outer-layer cells that are lost through wear and exposure to forces and the environment.

OBJECTIVE 5

Types of epithelial tissue as classified by shape

✔ **Note:** Epithelial tissue can be classified by the shape of its cells and by its tissue-layer arrangement—whether or not the tissue consists of a single layer of cells or multiple layers. In this objective and the next, you will study the three classifications by shape and the two classifications by tissue-layer arrangement.

a. Squamous (skwaw´-muhs) tissue—Tissue consisting of flat cells that somewhat resemble scales (see Figure 5 and Figure 8)

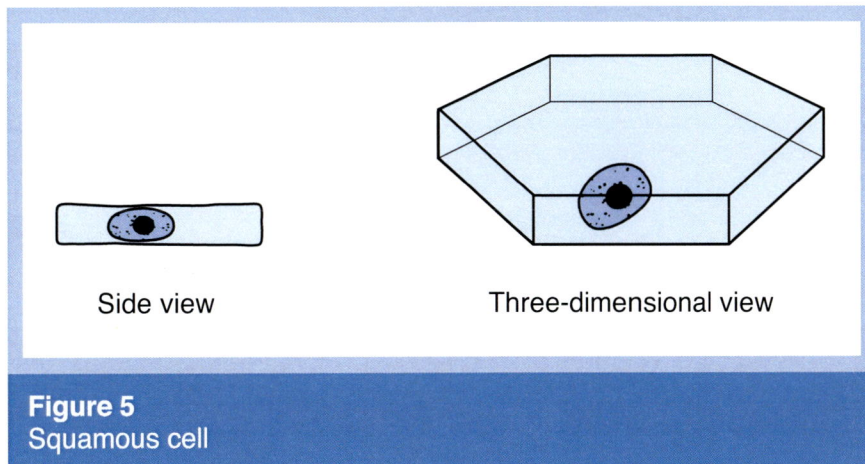

Side view   Three-dimensional view

Figure 5
Squamous cell

b. Cuboidal (kyu-boid´-uhl) tissue—Tissue consisting of cells that somewhat resemble square boxes, having dimensions approximately the same height, width, and depth (see Figure 6 and Figure 8)

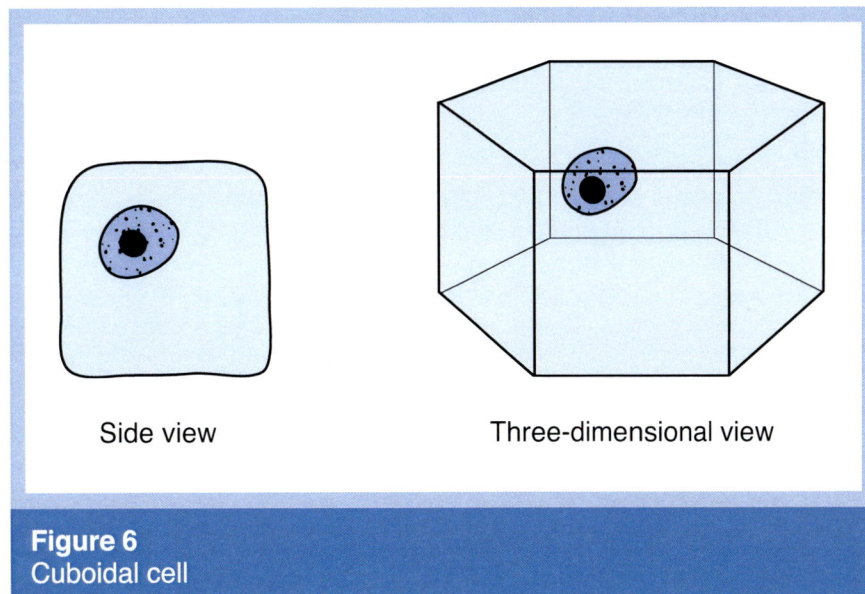

Side view   Three-dimensional view

Figure 6
Cuboidal cell

c.   Columnar (kuh-luhm´-nuhr) tissue—Tissue consisting of cells that somewhat resemble rectangular boxes, having one dimension that is longer than the others (see Figure 7 and Figure 8)

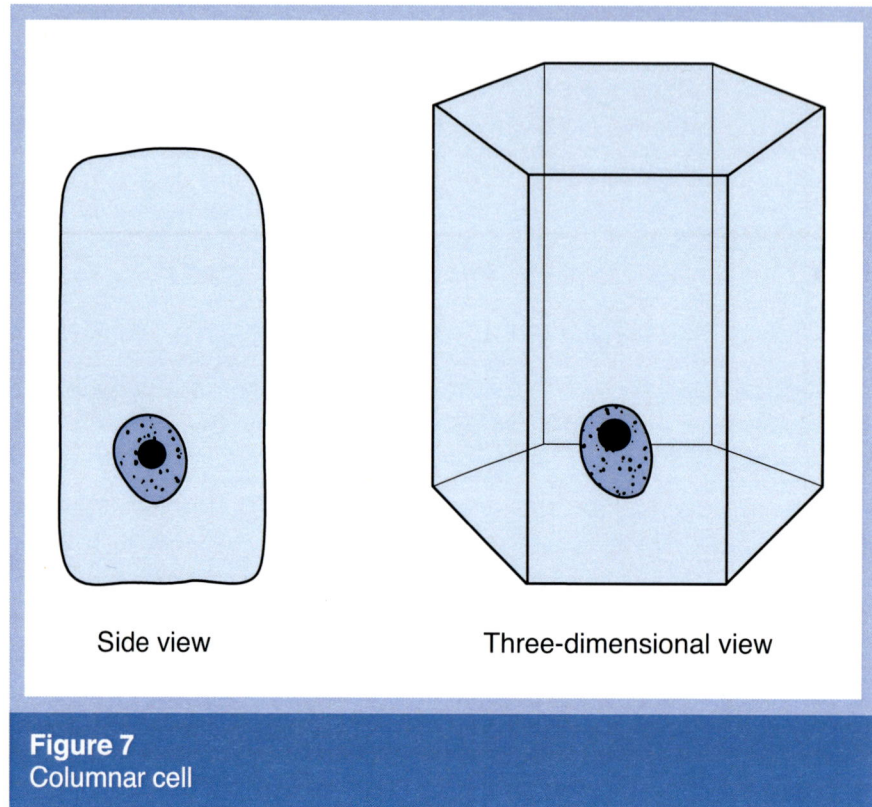

Side view   Three-dimensional view

Figure 7
Columnar cell

OBJECTIVE 6 | **Types of epithelial tissue as classified by tissue-layer arrangement**

a. Simple tissue—Tissue consisting of a single layer of cells

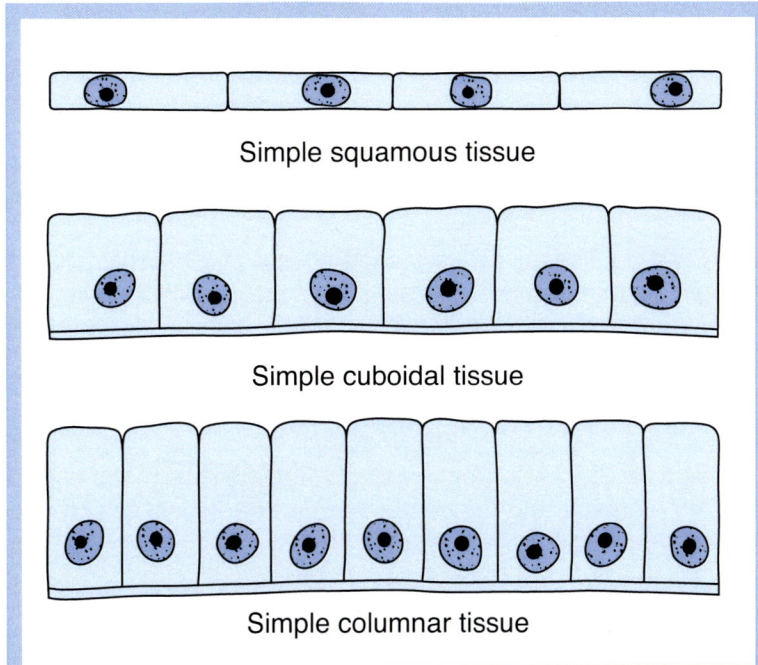

Figure 8
Simple tissue-layer arrangement

b. Stratified (strat´-uh-fid) tissue—Tissue consisting of more than one layer of cells

✔ **Note:** Only squamous cells form stratified tissue.

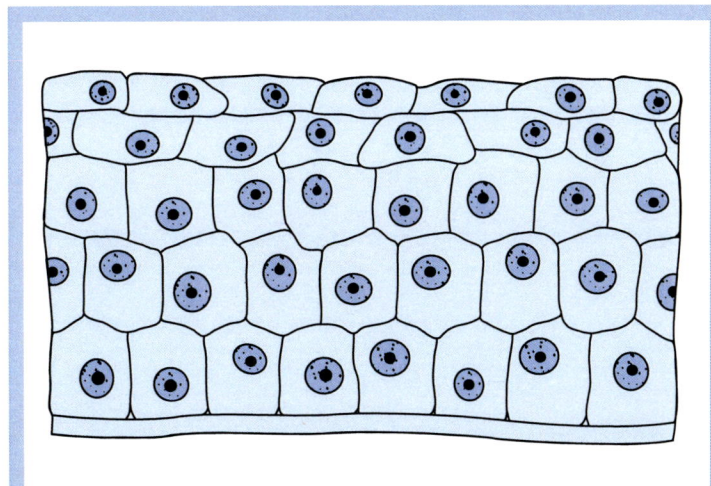

Figure 9
Stratified tissue-layer arrangement

Module 4-A: Tissues, Membranes, and Wound Healing

Classes of epithelial tissue and their functions

KEY TERM

Alveolus (al-ve´-uh-luhs)—One of many small sacs within the lungs in which the exchange of gases take place, absorbing oxygen and releasing carbon dioxide

---

a. Squamous tissue—Lines the blood vessels and the **alveoli**; the thinness of the tissue allows gases and chemicals to pass through the tissue

b. Cuboidal tissue—Lines glands such as the thyroid and salivary glands; the shape of the tissue promotes secretion of chemicals by the glands

c. Columnar tissue—Lines the stomach and intestines and secretes gastric juices and enzymes; some have cilia to sweep substances along, such as those that line the fallopian tubes and move an ovum toward the uterus

d. Simple tissue—Forms the single-layer linings of the capillaries, the thyroid gland, and the stomach; the thinness of the tissue allows gases and other substances to go in and out through the tissue

   Example: Oxygen flows through the capillary walls to the cells, while carbon dioxide flows from the cells into the capillaries

   ✔ **Note:** Simple tissue in the capillaries consists of squamous cells; simple tissue in the thyroid consists of cuboidal cells; and simple tissue in the stomach consists of columnar cells.

e. Stratified tissue—Forms the outer layer of the skin and the lining of the esophagus and the vagina; the thickness of the tissue and its secretions help to protect the body against pathogens

| OBJECTIVE 8 | **Types of connective tissue and their functions** |

KEY TERMS

Deep fascia (dep´ fash´-uh)—A band of connective tissue that covers or binds together body structures within body cavities

Dermis (duhr´-muhs)—The connective tissue that makes up the inner layer of skin

Eustachian tube (yu-sta´-she-uhn tub´)—A canal that allows air to pass between the middle-ear cavity and the nasopharyngeal cavity

Ligament (lig´-uh-muhnt)—A fibrous connective tissue that joins one bone to another

Platelet (plat´-luht)—A blood cell that helps the clotting process used to seal a wound

Tendon (ten´-duhn)—A fibrous connective tissue that connects muscle to bones

Trachea (tra´-ke-uh)—The windpipe

✔ **Note:** Connective tissue is the most-common tissue in the body. It protects and supports organs, transports substances, and binds body structures together. Different types of connective tissue have specific locations in the body and perform specific functions.

a. Reticular (ri-tik´-yuh-luhr) tissue—Located in the spleen, lymph nodes, and bone marrow; filters harmful substances from the blood and lymph

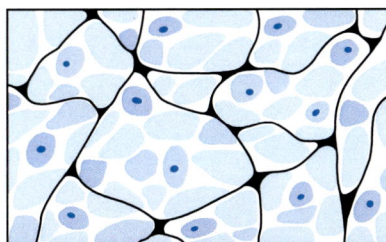

Figure 10
Reticular tissue

b. Areolar (uh-re´-uh-luhr) tissue—Located in loose accumulations between tissues and organs; connects tissues

Figure 11
Areolar tissue

c. Adipose (ad´-uh-pos) tissue—Located under the skin; provides padding, insulation, and a place to store fats

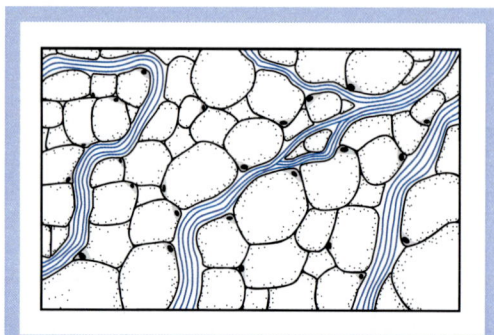

Figure 12
Adipose tissue

d. Fibrous (fi´-bruhs) tissue—Located in **tendons**, **ligaments**, **deep fascia**, **dermis**, and the kidneys; provides strong, flexible connections and the formation of scars

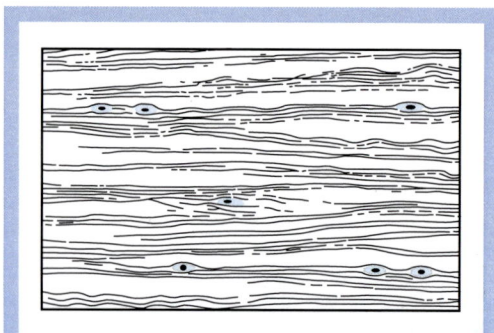

Figure 13
Fibrous tissue

e. Bone (bon´) tissue—Located in the skeleton; forms bones to support the body and protect organs and tissues

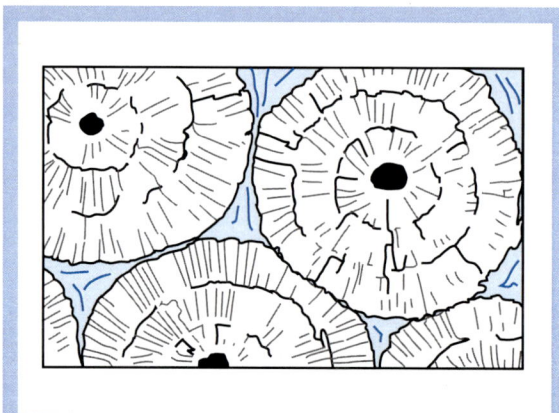

Figure 14
Bone tissue

f. Cartilage (kart´-uhl-ij) tissue—Located in the nose, ears, trachea, and eustachian tubes and at bone joints; provides a firm-but-not-rigid structure and padding between bones

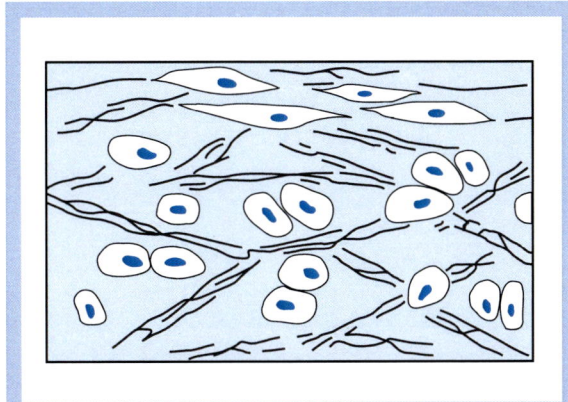

Figure 15
Cartilage tissue

g. Blood (bluhd´) tissue—Located throughout the blood system; transports materials, including oxygen, throughout the body and combats foreign organisms and cells

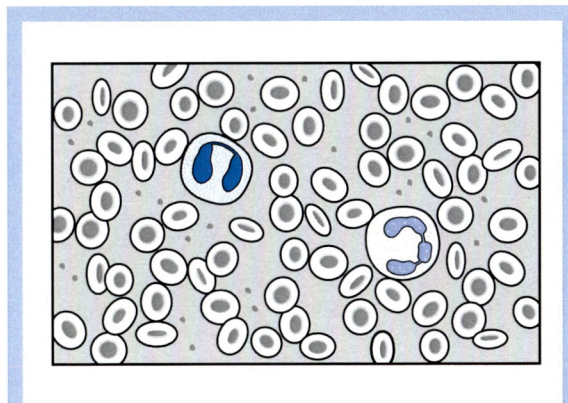

Figure 16
Blood tissue

h. Lymphatic (lim-fat´-ik) tissue—Located in the lymph nodes, spleen, tonsils, and thymus; forms certain types of white blood cells

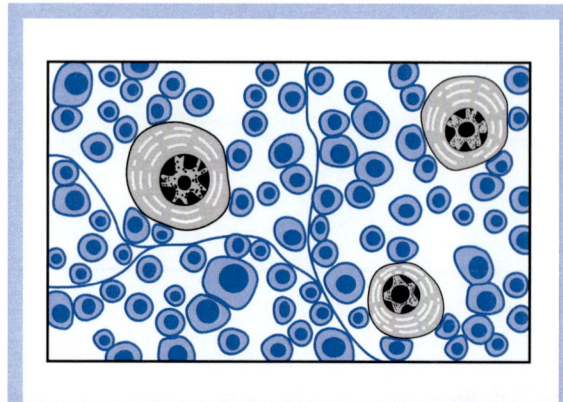

Figure 17
Lymphatic tissue

i. Myeloid (mi´-uh-loid) tissue—Located in the bone marrow; forms red and white blood cells and **platelets**

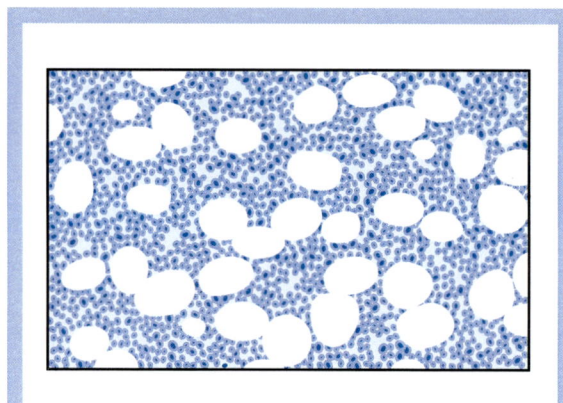

Figure 18
Myeloid tissue

j. Elastic (i-las´-tik) tissue—Located along the walls of the large arteries and alveoli in the lungs; helps in maintaining blood pressure in the blood system and in the exhalation of breath in the lungs

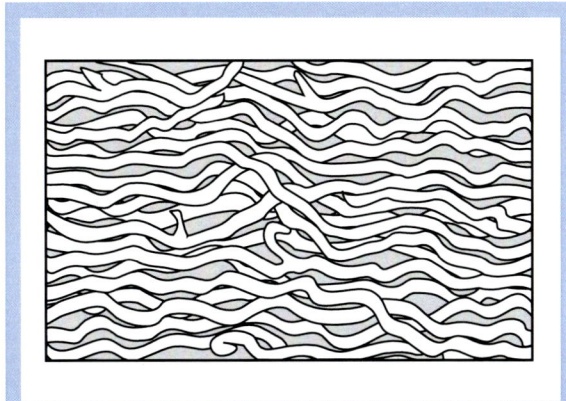

Figure 19
Elastic tissue

OBJECTIVE 9

Basic types of nerve tissue

a. Neurons (nu´-rawns)—The basic nerve-tissue cells of the nervous system that are capable of generating electrochemical impulses that carry information to and from the brain

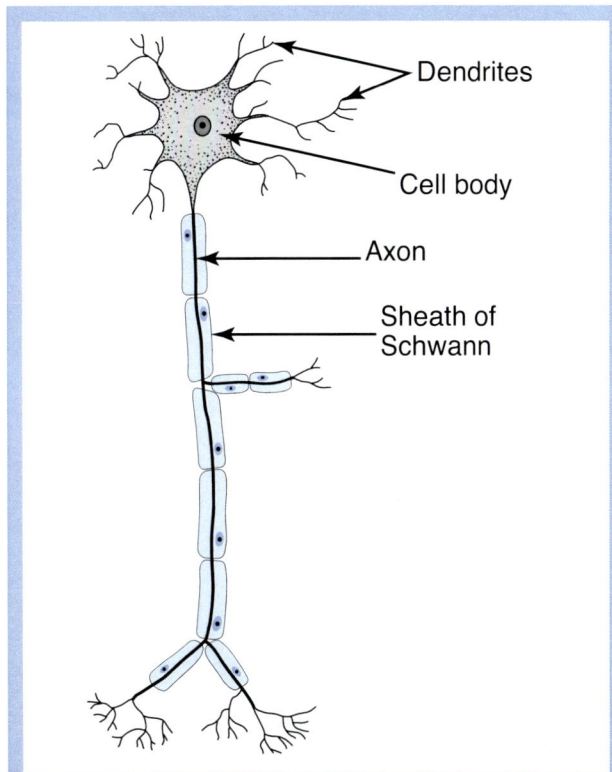

Dendrites

Cell body

Axon

Sheath of Schwann

Figure 20
Basic parts of a neuron

b. Neuroglia (nu-ro´-gle-uh)—The supporting- or connecting-tissue cells of the central nervous system

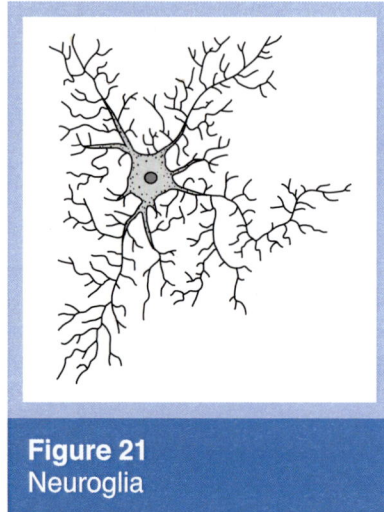

Figure 21
Neuroglia

OBJECTIVE 10

Functions of the basic parts of a neuron

✔ **Note:** Neurons consist of a cell body and two extensions: axons (ak´-sawns) and dendrites (den´-drits). A neuron will have one axon but may have several dendrites (see Figure 20 on the previous page).

a. Axon—Carries nervous-system impulses from the cell body

b. Dendrite—Carries nervous-system impulses to the cell body

c. Cell body—Performs metabolic and reproductive functions for the cell

OBJECTIVE 11

How neurons function in the nervous system

KEY TERM

Sheath (sheth´)—A covering, especially a loose-fitting one

a. Neurons are surrounded by specialized cells that form the **Sheath** of Schwann, which electrically isolates neurons (see Figure 20).

b. The axon of one neuron is separated from a dendrite of an adjoining neuron by a space called a *synapse* (sin´-aps).

c. Nerve-system impulses cannot cross the synapse unless it is filled with special chemicals called *neurotransmitters* (nur-o-tranz-mit´-uhrs).

d. There are three kinds of neurons as determined by their location and function: sensory, motor, and interneurons.

e. Sensory neurons, which are sometimes referred to as *afferent* (af´-uh-ruhnt) neurons, carry signals from receptors in the skin, skeletal muscles, joints, and organs to the central nervous system.

f. Motor neurons, which are sometimes referred to as *efferent* (ef´-uh-ruhnt) *neurons,* carry impulses from the central nervous system to effectors (i-fek´-tuhrs) that cause responses in the muscles and glands.

g. Interneurons, which are located in the central nervous system, carry either sensory or motor impulses or connect motor and sensory neurons and support higher-order functions such as thinking and learning.

OBJECTIVE 12

Functions of the types of neuroglia

KEY TERM

Cerebrospinal fluid (suh-re-bro-spin´-uhl flu´-uhd)—The tissue fluid that circulates around the brain and spinal cord

---

a. Oligodendrocytes (awl-i-go-den´-druh-sites)—Form the insulating sheath on neurons in the central nervous system

b. Microglia (mi-krawg´-li-uh)—Move so that they can locate and destroy damaged tissue and invading cells and organisms

c. Astrocytes (as´-truh-sites)—Prevent harmful chemicals from entering the brain from contaminated blood

d. Ependyma (ep-en´-di-muh)—Line the cavities in the brain and help to circulate **cerebrospinal fluid**

Module 4-A: Tissues, Membranes, and Wound Healing

| **Factors that determine muscle-tissue classifications**

> KEY TERMS
> _____
>
> **Cardiac** (kard´-e-ak)—Striated, involuntary muscle tissue that composes the walls of the heart
>
> **Involuntary**—Muscles that work automatically
>
> Example: Heart muscles
>
> **Skeletal** (skel´-uht-uhl)—Striated, voluntary muscle tissue attached to bones
>
> **Striated** (stri´-at-uhd)—Lined with grooves
>
> **Visceral** (vis´-uh-ruhl)—Smooth, involuntary muscle tissue that lines the walls of hollow organs
>
> **Voluntary** (vawl´-uhn-ter-e)—Muscles that are consciously controlled by the will of a person
>
> Example: Muscles that move an arm

a.   Structural composition—Whether the muscle tissue is **striated** or smooth (nonstriated) (see Figures 22 through 24))

b.   Level of conscious control—Whether the muscle is **voluntary** or **involuntary**

c.   Location—Whether the muscle tissue is **skeletal**, **visceral**, or **cardiac** (see Figures 22 through 24)

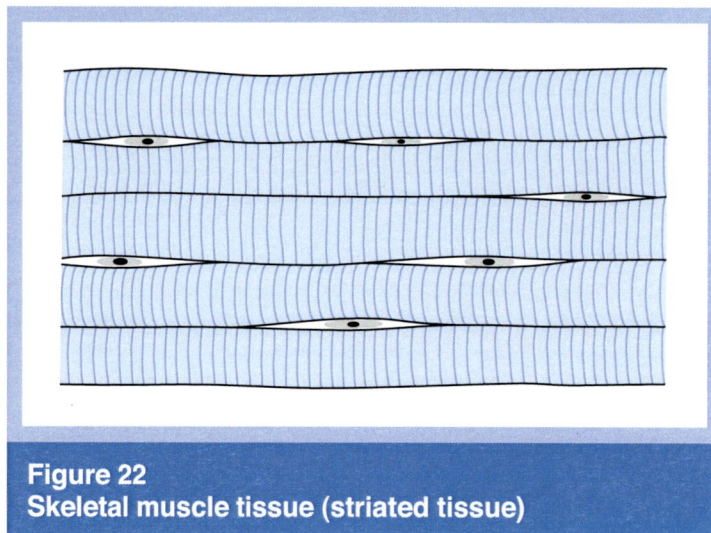

Figure 22
Skeletal muscle tissue (striated tissue)

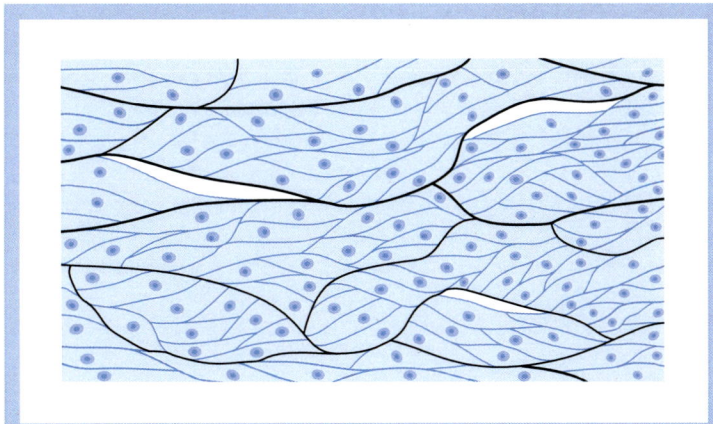

Figure 23
Visceral muscle tissue (smooth tissue)

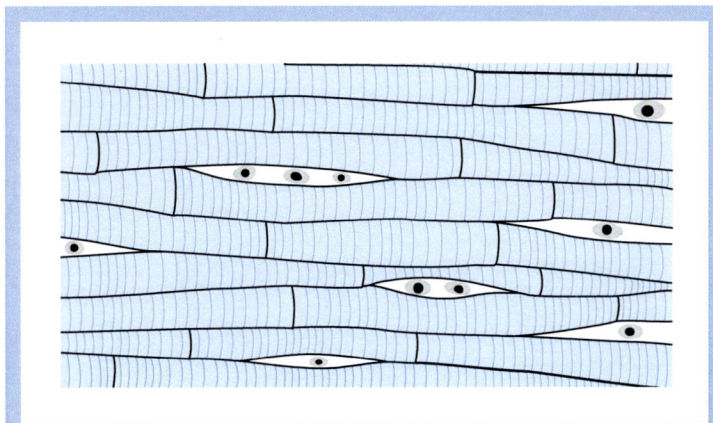

Figure 24
Cardiac muscle tissue (striated tissue)

| OBJECTIVE 14 | **Types of muscle contractions** |

✔ **Note:** Muscles create movement by contracting and relaxing. The most-popular explanation for how muscles contract is referred to as the *sliding-filament theory*. This theory is covered in Objective 15 and Objective 16.

a. Flexion (flek´-shuhn)—A movement that decreases the angle of a joint

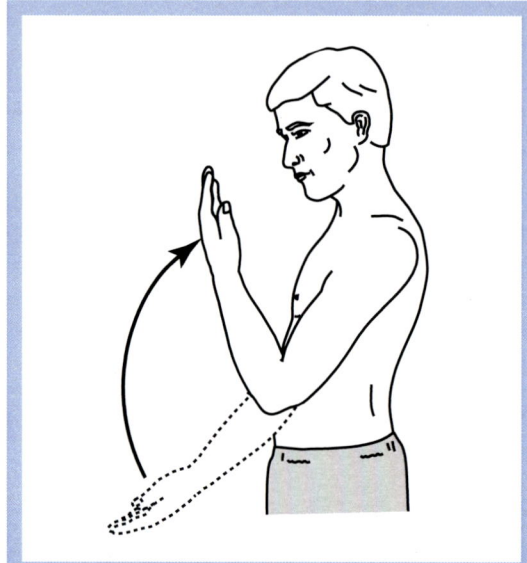

**Figure 25
Flexion of the elbow**

b. Extension (ik-sten´-chuhn)—A movement that increases the angle of a joint

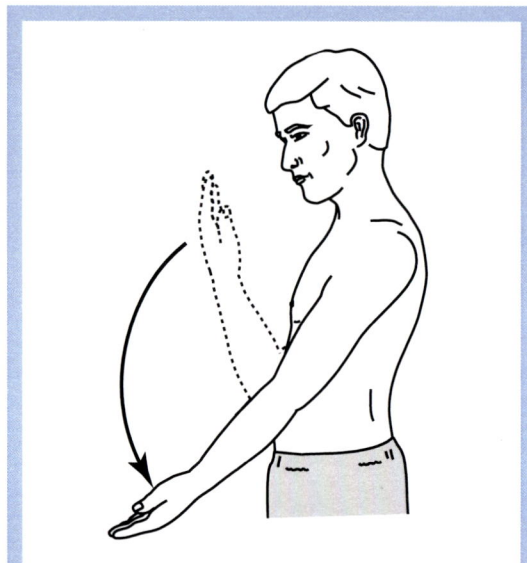

**Figure 26
Extension of the elbow**

c. Adduction (uh-duhk´-shuhn)—A movement of a limb toward the midline of the body

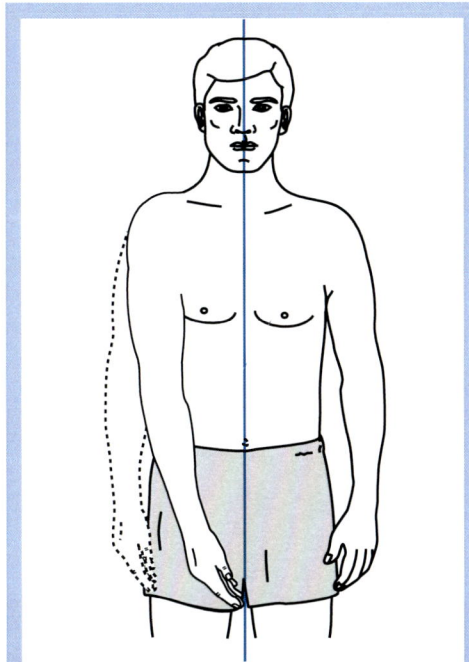

Figure 27
Adduction of the arm

d. Abduction (ab-duhk´-shuhn)—A movement of a limb away from the midline of the body

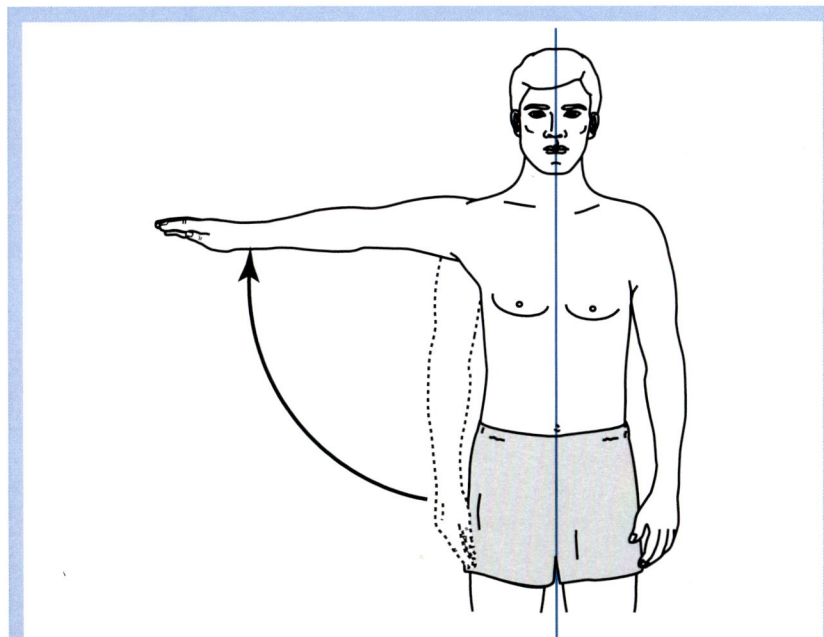

Figure 28
Abduction of the arm

e. Pronation (pro-na´-shuhn)—A rotating movement of the hand so that the palm faces backwards or downward; an inward and downward rotating motion of the foot

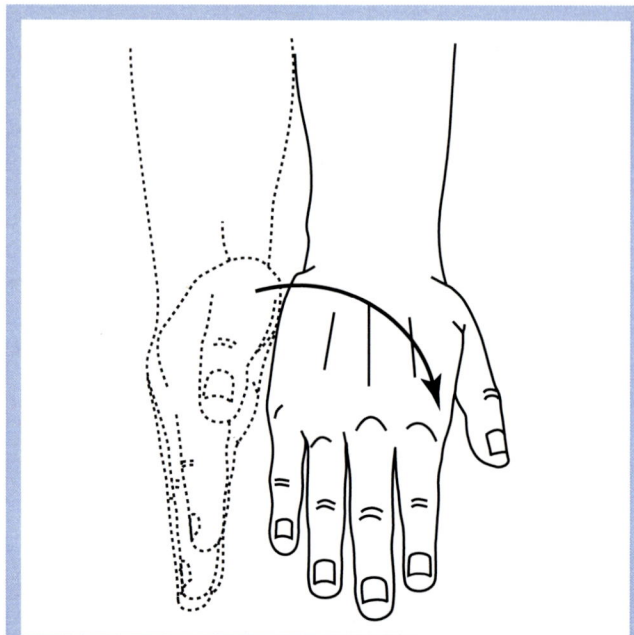

Figure 29
Pronation of the hand

f. Supination (su-puh-na´-shuhn)—A rotating movement of the forearm and hand so that the palm faces forward or upward; a corresponding movement of the foot and leg

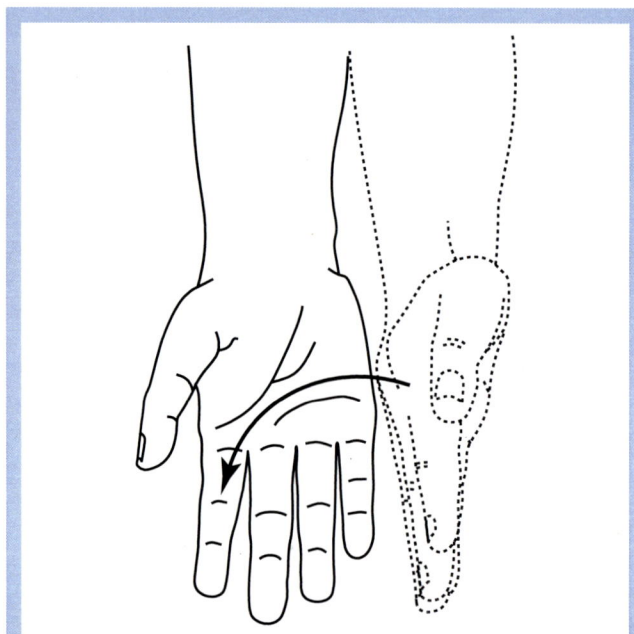

Figure 30
Supination of the hand

g.   Dorsiflexion (dor´-si-flek-shuhn)—A movement of a part of the body toward the back

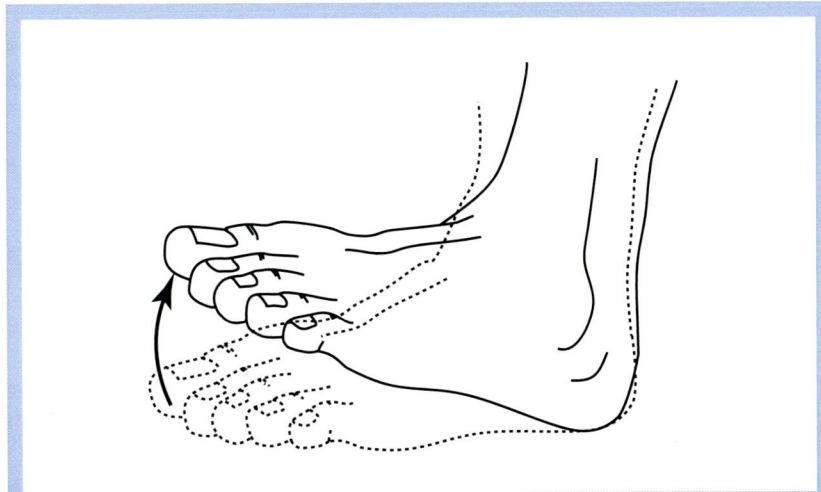

Figure 31
Dorsiflexion of the foot

h.   Plantar flexion (plant´-uhr flek´-shuhn)—A toe-down movement of the foot at the ankle

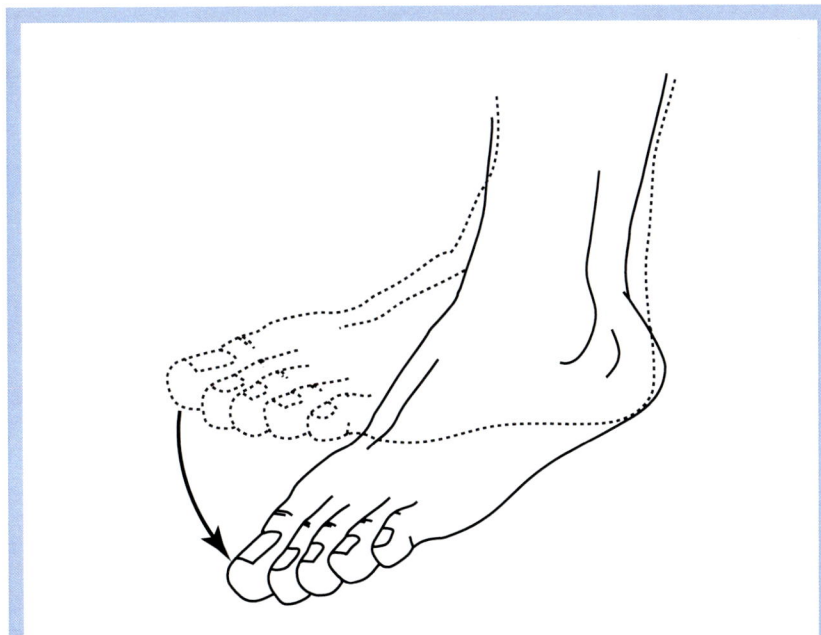

Figure 32
Plantar flexion

i. Rotation (ro-ta´-shuhn)—A rotating movement on an axis

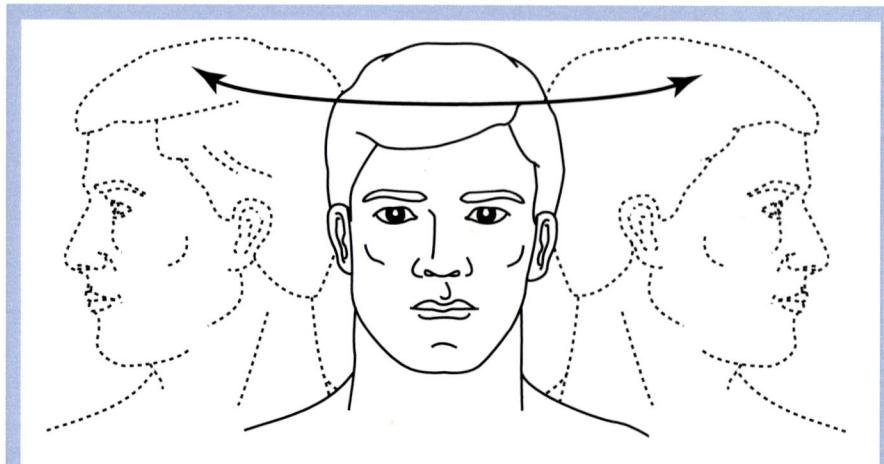

**Figure 33
Rotation of the head**

OBJECTIVE 15

The term *neuromuscular excitability*

Neuromuscular excitability (nur-o-muhs´-kyuh-luhr ik-sit-uh-bil´-uht-e)—The response of muscle tissue to stimulation by the nervous system

✔ **Note:** Basically, the process of neuromuscular excitability involves sending an electrical impulse to selected muscle tissue to cause the muscle to contract so that a desired movement can be accomplished.

OBJECTIVE 16

Neuromuscular-excitability response (sliding-filament theory)

KEY TERMS

Filament (fil´-uh-muhnt)—A threadlike, flexible structure

Permeable (puhr´-me-uh-buhl)—Capable of allowing substances to penetrate a structure

✔ **Note:** Permeability is often a characteristic of tissues and membranes within the body. Most are selectivity permeable—that is, they allow some substances to pass through and keep other substances from permeating, thus serving as a filter. In the case described, the fiber membrane normally keeps sodium ions from passing through until ACh binds to the receptors. Then the intercellular spaces relax and the sodium ions are able to move into the fibers.

---

a. Each muscle fiber is connected to the motor axon of a motor nerve.

b. The point where the neuron terminates on a muscle fiber is referred to as the *neuromuscular junction.*

c. Sacs in the end of the nerve contain a neurotransmitter called *acetylcholine* (uh-set-uhl-ko´-len) (ACh).

d. The sarcolemma (sar-kuh-lem´-uh) membrane of the muscle fiber has receptors that are sensitive to ACh.

e. During a normally relaxed state, the outer membrane of a muscle fiber is positively charged due to an abundance of positive sodium ions (Na^+) and the core of the fiber is negatively charged due to an abundance of negative potassium ions (K^-).

f. A nerve impulse arriving at the motor axon causes a release of ACh.

g. ACh binds to the receptors in the fiber membrane, causing it to become **permeable** to sodium and allowing the sodium ions to move toward the core of the fiber.

h. An arrangement of **filaments** with the muscle fiber—called a sarcomere (sar´-kuh-mir)—shorten to contract the fiber.

i. Because virtually all of the fibers in the muscle are undergoing the same neuromuscular excitation, the entire muscle contracts.

j. As long as the impulses continue, the muscle will remain contracted in a condition known as *tetanus* (tet´-nuhs).

k. When the nerve impulses cease, the sarcolemma releases cholinesterase (ko-luh-nes´-tuh-ras), which inactivates the ACh.

l. The sodium ions flow back to the surface of the fiber so that it returns to its normal charge state of a positively charged membrane and a negatively charged core.

Module 4-A: Tissues, Membranes, and Wound Healing

Locations of the main types of membranes

KEY TERMS

Bursa (buhr´-suh)—A sac of synovial fluid that helps to reduce friction between a bone and tendon

Dermis (duhr´-muhs)—The inner layer of skin consisting of papillary and reticular layers and containing blood and lymphatic vessels, nerves and nerve endings, glands, and hair follicles

Epidermis (ep-uh-duhr´-muhs)—The outer layer of skin made up of an outer, dead portion and a deeper, living, cellular portion

Hypodermis (hi-puh-duhr´-muhs)—The layer of areolar tissue and fat that lies beneath the dermis

---

✔ **Note:** As you learned in Objective 4, a membrane is a thin layer of tissue that covers a surface, lines a cavity, or divides a space. A membrane is composed of epithelial or connective tissue. The four main types of membranes are discussed below.

a. Mucous (myu´-kuhs) membrane—Lines cavities and passages that open to the exterior

   ✔ **Note:** The nasal passages, for example, are lined with mucous membrane. The mucus secreted by the membrane helps to trap dirt, dust, pollen, and other substances to keep them from reaching the lungs.

b. Serous membrane—Lines the closed cavities of the body

c. Synovial (suh-no´-ve-uhl) membrane—Lines the skeletal joints, tendons, and **bursae**

d. Cutaneous (kyu-ta´-ne-uhs) membrane—Covers the body as skin

   ✔ **Note:** The skin consists of three main layers: the **epidermis,** the **dermis,** and the **hypodermis.**

Functions of the main types of membranes

KEY TERMS

Parietal (puh-ri´-uht-uhl)—Of or pertaining to the outer wall of a cavity or organ
Visceral (vis´-uh-ruhl)—Of or pertaining to the viscera, or internal organs in the abdominal cavity

---

a. Mucous membrane—Forms a selective filter that allows some substances to enter the body while keeping others out; secretes mucus to keep its cells moist, to lubricate its surfaces, and to trap foreign particles

b. Serous membrane—Provides the **visceral** layer that covers organs enclosed in cavities; provides the **parietal** layer that lines cavities; secretes serous fluid to serve as a lubricant and pad between visceral and parietal layers

c. Synovial membrane—Secretes synovial fluid to provide lubrication and moisture

d. Cutaneous membrane—Secretes sweat and wastes to help maintain homeostasis

OBJECTIVE 19

The term *organ*

Organ—A structure consisting of two or more tissues that performs a specific function for the body

OBJECTIVE 20

Types of tissues and membranes found in selected organs

KEY TERMS

Endocardium (en-duh-kard´-e-uhm)—The lining of the heart chambers
Myocardium (mi-uh-kard´-e-uhm)—The thick middle layer of the heart wall
Pericardium (per-uh-kard´-e-uhm)—A sac that surrounds the heart
Peritoneum (per-uht-uhn-e´-uhm)—An extensive serous membrane that covers the entire abdominal wall of the body

---

a. Heart—Simple squamous epithelial tissue, fibrous connective tissue, cardiac muscle tissue, serous membrane

   ✔ **Note:** Simple squamous epithelial tissue forms the **endocardium**; fibrous connective tissue forms the fibrous **pericardium**; cardiac muscle tissue forms the **myocardium**; serous membrane forms the serous pericardium.

b. Stomach—Fibrous connective tissue, smooth muscle tissue, mucous membrane, serous membrane

   ✔ **Note:** Serous membrane forms the **peritoneum**.

c. Nerves—Nerve tissue

d. Brain—Nerve tissue

e. Lungs—Elastic connective tissue, epithelial tissue

OBJECTIVE 21

How organ systems function

a. Organs are collections of tissues that are organized in such a way that they are able to perform specific functions.

b. The overall goal of these functions is to maintain a state of homeostasis in the body.

c. Each organ system monitors one or more conditions internal to the body or in the body's external environment.

   Examples: Internal body temperature and external environmental temperature

d.   The organs have feedback mechanisms that send signals to the central nervous system (CNS) about the conditions that they monitor.

e.   The CNS provides response signals to organs in order to actuate regulation mechanisms designed to return the body to homeostasis.

> ✔ **Note:** If the body is too hot, for example, the CNS may cause the body to sweat. Sweat carries heat from the body and air moving across the damp skin will make it feel cooler. If the body is too cold, the CNS may cause it to shiver to generate heat. If the body needs more oxygen, as during strenuous exercise, the CNS will cause faster respiration and a faster heartbeat. If a person ingests food, the CNS will direct the stomach to secrete gastric juices.

f.   Many of the response mechanisms involve physical or chemical reactions.

g.   Organs are also involved in the transport of materials throughout the body.

> Examples: Blood carries oxygen and digested nutrients through the body, the digestive tract moves food so that it can be absorbed, the lymph system carries lymphocytes and monocytes to the bloodstream

OBJECTIVE 22

Abnormalities in organ development

✔ **Note:** Most developmental abnormalities in organs result from genetic defects or hormonal dysfunctions.

a.   Aplasia (uh-pla´-zhuh)—A developmental failure resulting in the absence of an organ or tissue

b.   Hypoplasia (hi-po-pla´-zhuh)—An incomplete development or underdevelopment of an organ or tissue, which is usually the result of a decrease in the number of cells

c.   Atrophy (a´-truh-fe)—A wasting or diminution of size or activity of a part of the body, usually the result of an abnormal decrease in cell size

d.   Hypertrophy (hi-puhr´-truh-fe)—An increase in the size of an organ caused by an increase in the size of the cells rather than the number of cells

e.   Hyperplasia (hi-puhr-pla´-zhuh)—An increase in the number of cells of a body part

f.   Dysplasia (dis-pla´-zhuh)—Any abnormal development of tissues or organs

g.   Anaplasia (an-uh-pla´-zhuh)—A change in the structure or orientation of cells characterized by the production of abnormal, undifferentiated cells

> ✔ **Note:** Anaplasia is characteristic of a malignancy.

| OBJECTIVE 23 | **Types of injuries that can damage tissue** |

> KEY TERMS
>
> **Aseptic** (a-sep´-tik)—Free from pathogens
> **Extrinsic** (ek-strin´-zik)—Outside of and not part of (the body)
> **Incision** (in-sizh´-uhn)—A smooth-sided wound, especially one made during surgery
> **Trauma** (trau´-muh)—An injury to living tissue caused by an extrinsic agent

a. Surgical **incision**—The separation of intact tissue by a surgeon using **aseptic** techniques

b. **Traumatic** wound—An injury to living body tissue caused by an **extrinsic** agent

Examples: Cuts, abrasions, punctures, crushing

c. Chemical reaction—An injury to body tissue that is the result of a response of the body to exposure to a chemical

> ✔ **Note:** There are a number of reactions to chemicals, both internally and externally. External exposure may lead to chemical burns, rashes, interruptions in chemical processes, and other problems. Internally, chemicals can lead to immediate death from toxin or interference with cell functioning, as with the consumption of alcohol. External chemicals can be absorbed through the skin, eyes, mucous membranes, and other portals of entry to cause internal reactions.

d. Frostbite—Local damage to tissue as a result of exposure to low temperatures

e. Bacterial infection—The death of cells as a result of the action of microorganisms

f. Burn—Damage to tissue due to exposure to a high-energy source

Examples: Thermal burns, radiation burns, friction burns

| OBJECTIVE 24 | **Types of traumatic wounds** |

> KEY TERM
>
> **Subdermal** (suhb-duhr´-muhl)—Below the skin

a. Abrasion (uh-bra´-zhuhn)—A wound caused by friction between the tissue and a mechanical force

> ✔ **Note:** *Scrape* is a common term for abrasion.

b. Contusion (kuhn-tu´-zhuhn)—A wound caused by a force that does not break the skin but is sufficient to cause damage to **subdermal** tissues

> ✔ **Note:** *Bruise* is a common term for contusion.

c. Avulsion (uh-vuhl´-shuhn)—A wound in which skin and underlying tissue are partially or completely torn away

   d.   Incised (in-sizd´) wound—A wound with smooth edges caused by a sharp surface

   e.   Lacerated (las´-uh-rat-uhd) wound—A wound with irregular edges

   f.   Puncture (puhn{k}´-chuhr) wound—A wound with little surface area that has been made by a sharp, slender object

       Example: The wound created at a needle injection site

   g.   Perforated (puhr´-fuh-rat-uhd) wound—A wound caused by an object passing completely through the body or a portion of the body

       Example: The wound created when a bullet enters and exits a portion of the body

   h.   Crush wound—A wound that is caused by pressure that is sufficient to alter or destroy tissue structure

       ✔ **Note:** A crush wound may cause the skin to rupture, break bones, burst blood vessels, and rupture or severely displace cells.

OBJECTIVE 25

Causes of the characteristics of the inflammation response

KEY TERMS

Fibrin (fi´-bruhn)—A stringy, insoluble protein produced in the clotting process

Kinin (ki´-nuhn)—A polypeptide hormone that forms in the tissues and has its chief effect on smooth muscle

Rubor (ru´-bor)—The medical term for redness

✔ **Note:** In Module 3-A, you studied the body's defenses against infection and learned that inflammation is one of those defense mechanisms. This objective provides more details of how that process works.

   a.   **Rubor**—Immediately upon the occurrence of an insult to a site, the blood vessels in that area constrict and then dilate, allowing blood to pool in the area as the vessels fill and blood is unable to flow quickly through the undilated vessels beyond the injured area.

   b.   **Heat**—White blood cells begin to accumulate in the injury site, attaching to the blood-vessel walls and leading the body to release stored white blood cells. The white blood cells begin to pass through the walls of the blood vessels to fill the interstitial spaces, attracted by chemicals such as **kinins** released by the injured tissues. The purpose of the white blood cells is to attack pathogens that may have entered the wound. They also fill the area with concentrated warmth.

   c.   **Swelling**—As white blood cells, chemicals, fluids that leak from damaged blood vessels and cells, and other inflammatory exudate enter the interstitial areas, the injury site begins to bulge. Certain proteins in the interstitial solution transform into **fibrin** to form clots that seal the area. This helps to isolate the site so that pathogens are contained and infection is more easily prevented. This accumulation of body fluid is referred to as *edema* (i-de´-muh).

d. Pain—The inflammatory exudate, especially the chemicals released by the injured cells, result in pain. The pain may help to protect the site by telling the organism to give it attention and to be careful with it.

OBJECTIVE 26

Phases in the body's healing response

KEY TERMS

Collagen (kawl´-uh-juhn)—A protein that composes strong fibers in several types of connective tissue

Fibrinogen (fi-brin´-uh-juhn)—A protein produced by the liver that is converted into fibrin by thrombin to promote clotting at an injury site

Fibroblast (fib´-ruh-blast)—A connective tissue cell that produces collagen and elastin fibers

Leukocyte (lu´-kuh-site)—Another term for a white blood cell

Scar (skar´)—A mark left on the skin as a result of an injury

Tensile strength (ten´-sil stren{k}th´)—A material's resistance to being torn apart by opposing forces

---

a. Lag phase (substrate phase)

- Exudate containing blood, lymph, and **fibrinogen** begins clotting and loosely binds the cut edges together.

- Fibrin, clotting blood, and serum protein dry out, forming a scab to seal the wound.

- **Leukocytes** remove bacteria and damaged tissue debris.

b. Healing phase (proliferative phase)

- **Fibroblasts** multiply rapidly to bridge the wound gap, secreting fiber-forming **collagen**.

- **Tensile strength** grows rapidly as the collagen network of fibers builds.

- New cells form to replace cells that were damaged by the injury.

c. Maturation phase (remodeling phase)

- **Scar** tissue forms.

- The collagen re-forms into cross-links that further increase tensile strength.

- As collagen density increases, the vascular makeup of the site decreases, reducing blood flow in the area so that the color of the site becomes closer to normal.

Module 4-A: Tissues, Membranes, and Wound Healing

Types of treatment responses in the treatment of wounds

KEY TERMS

Approximate (uh-prawk´-suh-mat)—To bring two tissue surfaces close together, as in the repair of a wound

Granulation (gran-yuh-la´-shuhn) **tissue**—Any soft, pink, fleshy projections that form during the healing process in a wound not healing by first intention

✔ **Note:** Granulation tissue consists of many capillaries surrounded by fibrous collagen.

Postoperative (po-stawp´-uh-ruht-iv)—Following a surgical procedure

Primary (pri´-mer-e) **union**—The situation in which severed tissue is essentially reunited with the tissue from which it was originally separated and that the healing process begins without disruptions from swelling, contamination, infection, and other factors

Suture (su´-chuhr)—A stitch placed in tissue to hold the sides of a wound together during the healing process

---

✔ **Note:** The process of healing is largely dependent on how a wound is treated and how quickly. Wound treatment is performed with the intention of preventing infection and promoting healing. Ideally, after treatment the sides of a wound are properly **approximated**, the site has not become deformed by swelling, and treatment has occurred before **granulation tissue** has developed. Careful closure of the wound after trauma is then called *first-intention treatment*; second- and third-intention treatments are less-responsive treatments of wounds.

a. First-intention treatment

- The wound is closed with a **suture** soon after the incision or trauma.

- There is no **postoperative** swelling.

- There is no serous discharge or infection.

    ✔ **Note:** Wounds accompanied by infection or that are not properly healing are often accompanied by a watery discharge that oozes from the wound. The discharge consists of water and other body fluids and the by-products of the body's defense mechanisms, such as white blood cells, dead cells, fragments of pathogens, etc.

- There is minimal separation of the wound edges.

- There is minimal scar formation.

- Healing is by **primary union**.

- Healing is relatively fast.

b. Second-intention treatment

- The wound is not closed with a suture.

- There is excessive loss of tissue or poorly approximated tissue.

- There is serous discharge and infection.

- There is excessive separation of the wound edges.

- There is significant scar formation.

- Healing may produce a weak union with granulation tissue forming in the bottom of the wound and slowly contracting the wound together as it builds up.

- Healing takes longer than normal.

c. Third-intention treatment

- The wound is closed with a suture, but it is not closed immediately after the incision or trauma.

- There may be loss of tissue due to infections or complications of the healing process.

- There is serous discharge and infection, often after an initial suturing.

- There is excessive separation of the wound edges due to disruption of the healing process.

- There is usually a deeper and wider scar formation.

- Healing may produce a weak union with some granulation forming in the infection site or area of poor healing.

- Healing takes longer than normal.

OBJECTIVE 28   **Factors that affect the wound-healing process**

KEY TERM

Vitality (vi-tal´-uht-e)—The ability to carry out life functions efficiently

a. Age—The body's ability to heal declines as a person ages

✔ **Note:** A number of conditions brought on by age interfere with the healing process. Tissue **vitality** decreases with age. Organs involved in the healing process may not be functioning at their full capacity. For example, an age-weakened heart and clogged arteries reduce the flow of blood to the wound site, while an elderly person's digestive system may not efficiently process the nutrients required for healing. The immune system may become less able to fend off infection with increased age.

b. Nutritional status—The production of cells and tissues as part of the healing process requires an adequate supply of the proper nutrients.

✔ **Note:** Zinc, protein, and carbohydrates and vitamins A, B, and C are required for proper healing. If any one of these nutrients is missing or inadequate in a patient's diet, the surgical wound will not heal as quickly.

c. Electrolyte balance—The transport to the wound site of nutrients, oxygen, hormones, and other substances that promote healing depends on the pathways provided by blood and interstitial fluids.

✔ **Note:** The loss of fluids and the improper balance of electrolytes interfere with the healing process by slowing down the transport of oxygen, hormones, and other substances and by disrupting cellular metabolism. The diffusion of nutrients at the cellular level is efficient only when the concentrations of solutes is balanced.

d. Physical condition—The good circulation and lack of fat associated with good physical conditioning reduce the chances of a wound becoming infected.

✔ **Note:** Excessive fat deposits make it difficult to get good wound closure and make the wound very vulnerable to trauma and infection. Good physical conditioning often means a good diet and adequate exercise for better overall health.

e. Surgical technique—Good surgical technique complements the body's healing functions while poor surgical technique interferes with the healing process.

✔ **Note:** Poor antiseptic practices can lead to infections, while improperly performed incisions or suturing can lead to a poorly closed wound, tearing of sutures, or herniation (see Objective 29). Healing is promoted when the depth and the size of the incision are kept to a minimum. The use of correct wound-closure technique can ensure that the tissue fuses well and has minimal scarring.

f. Infection—The fighting of an infection reduces the amount of nutrients, oxygen, and other substances that can be involved in the healing process; further, the pathogens may produce toxins that interfere with the body's chemicals that are involved in healing.

✔ **Note:** Tissues that are combating infection are slow to heal because the infection interferes with the healing process. The body's resources may be diverted away from the healing process to fight the infecting pathogens.

g. Therapy (ther´-uh-pe)—Treatment provided to the patient through therapy may include medications or procedures that either slow or improve the healing process.

✔ **Note:** Certain drugs, radiation, and other forms of treatment can affect the blood supply and can interfere with normal cell metabolism. On the other hand, physical therapy may include exercises that promote good circulation or a drug may reduce the chances of infection.

h. Complications (kawm´-pluh-ka-shuhns)—Outside influences not directly related to the surgery can interfere with wound healing.

 ✔ **Note:** Conditions that stress the suture, such as coughing or nausea, and infections unrelated to the primary site can slow the healing process. Some patients may have additional injuries or illnesses that divert healing resources from the surgical wound site (see Objective 29).

i. Exercise—The improved circulation that comes with exercise helps to deliver oxygen, nutrients, and other resources required for healing to the wound.

 ✔ **Note:** While exercise is helpful, it should be appropriate to the patient's condition and surgery so that the sutures are not stressed.

OBJECTIVE 29 | **Factors that present possible complications to the wound-healing process**

KEY TERMS

Dehiscence (di-his´-uhns)—The separation of the layers of a surgical wound

Evisceration (i-vis-uh-ra´-shuhn)—The extrusion of internal organs or viscera through a dehiscence

Eventration (e-vuhn-tra´-shuhn)—The partial protrusion of the abdominal contents through an opening in the abdominal wall

Purulent (pyur´-uh-luhnt)—Containing pus

---

a. Hemorrhage (hem´-uh-rij)—The loss of a large amount of blood in a short time caused by a failure of open blood vessels to adequately clot or to remain sealed

 ✔ **Note:** Clotting is an important part of the healing process because it helps to seal the wound. However, conditions such as hemophilia and anemia may prevent the blood from clotting properly. The loss of blood that results from hemorrhaging also reduces the amount of oxygen and nutrients that are available to the injured area and that are needed to promote healing.

b. Sinus-tract formation—The development of channels that permit the escape of **purulent** materials from pockets of pus and other fluids

 ✔ **Note:** Pockets of pus harbor the potential for infections to develop, and sinus tracts keep tissues separated that must be knit together during the healing process.

c. Hematoma (he-muh-to´-muh)—A swelling or tumor that contains blood that is generally clotted

 ✔ **Note:** A hematoma is similar to a sinus tract in that it creates a physical separation between tissues that must grow together. Hematomas also represent an area of reduced blood circulation that slows the healing process.

d. Infection—The presence of pathogens in a wound site

✔ **Note:** Infecting pathogens rob a wound site of nutrition and interfere with the normal functioning of cells. This interference may include disruption of the chemical processes involved in healing and reduction of the reproductive activities of the cells that are required to replace dead cells.

e. Herniation—A protrusion of an organ or tissue structure into a wound site

✔ **Note:** Herniation can lead to a number of complications. Like hematomas and sinus tracts, a protruding organ can force its way between tissue layers that are trying to rejoin. The pressure of the hernia can restrict blood flow, thus delaying the healing process. The hernia itself may lead to the development of other conditions, including infections, that reduce the healing resources that are available to the primary site. Depending on the organ involved, herniation may prevent the normal functioning of organs that support the healing process. For example, a herniated bowel may reduce the efficiency of digestion, a process that is vital in supplying nutrients to the body. Without proper digestion of food, proteins and vitamins that are necessary to build new cells may not enter the blood supply.

f. Wound disruption—One of the conditions—**dehiscence**, **evisceration**, or **eventration**—that interrupts the wound-healing process

✔ **Note:** Wound disruption is one of various conditions that can occur to the post-surgical patient. Generally, dehiscence, evisceration, and eventration are the result of a patient's not following postoperative-care instructions, causing the sutures to tear or the displacement of organs due to weakened tissues. Occasionally, wound disruption occurs due to poor surgical technique. Disruption usually occurs between the fourth and sixth postoperative day.

OBJECTIVE 30

Classifications of surgical wounds

KEY TERMS

Elective (i-lek´-tiv) **procedure**—An operation done by choice as opposed to being performed as an emergency

Nonpurulent (nawn-pyur´-uh-luhnt)—Without pus

Perforated (puhr´-fuh-rat-uhd) **organ**—An organ punctured in such a way that the contents of the organ could exude onto other structures

---

a. Clean (Class I)

• Has an expected infection rate of 1 to 5 percent

✔ **Note:** The percentages used in this objective indicate an estimated range of infection. A rate of 1 to 5 percent, for example, means that for every 100 surgeries done under the conditions described, one to five patients will develop infections.

• Involves an **elective procedure** done under ideal conditions

- Exhibits primary closure with no drainage

- Was not subjected to breaks in aseptic technique

- Shows no inflammation

- Did not require entry into alimentary, genitourinary, or respiratory tracts or oropharyngeal cavity

  ✔ **Note:** These sites are likely to contain microbes that can cause infections, including residential flora that promote health in their intended sites but may cause problems elsewhere.

b. Clean/contaminated (Class II)

- Has an expected infection rate of 8 to 11 percent

- Involves an internal procedure done under near-ideal conditions

- Exhibits normal drainage during procedure

- Was subjected to minor breaks in aseptic technique

- Shows no inflammation

- Required entry into alimentary, genitourinary, or respiratory tract or oropharyngeal cavity under controlled conditions

c. Contaminated (Class III)

- Has an expected infection rate of 15 to 20 percent

- Involves an internal procedure done under less-than-ideal conditions

- Started as an open, fresh, traumatic wound less than four hours old

- Was subjected to major breaks in aseptic technique

- Shows acute, **nonpurulent** inflammation

- Required entry that resulted in gross spillage or contamination from the gastrointestinal tract, entry into the biliary tract with infected bile present, entry into the genitourinary tract with urine present, or similar contamination

d. Infected (Class IV)

- Has an expected infection rate of 27 to 40 percent

- Involves an internal procedure done under less-than-ideal conditions

- Exhibits primary closure with no drainage

- Was subjected to microbial contamination in the operative field before the procedure

- Shows acute bacterial inflammation that may be purulent or be a known clinical infection

- Involves exposure to a **perforated organ**, such as a bowel

Glossary of Key Terms

Acid (as´-uhd)—A substance that releases a hydrogen ion when dissolved

Allergy (al´-uhr-je)—A condition of being highly sensitive to foreign substances that enter the body often because the person's immune system does not respond to the antigen of the substance

Alveolus (al-ve´-uh-luhs)—One of many small sacs within the lungs in which the exchange of gases take place, absorbing oxygen and releasing carbon dioxide

Amebic dysentery (uh-me´-bik dis-uhn´-ter-e)—A condition of severe diarrhea often accompanied by blood and mucus that results from an infection of protozoa

Anabolism (uh-nab´-uh-liz-uhm)—The process of chemical synthesis in which smaller molecules are combined to produce larger molecules

Anesthetize (uh-nes´-thuh-tiz)—To create in a patient a loss of sensation, with or without a loss of consciousness; to create a condition of anesthesia (an-uhs-the´-zhuh) in a patient; to administer an anesthetic (an-uhs-thet´-ik)

Antibiotic (ant-i-bi-awt´-ik)—A special medication that slows or stops the growth of certain microorganisms

Antibody (ant´-i-bawd-e)—A protein molecule that will bind to foreign substances in the body; a specialized protein produced in the blood plasma in response to bacteria, viruses, or other antigenic substances

Antiseptic (ant-uh-sep´-tik)—A chemical used to destroy or reduce the growth of pathogens on a person

Approximate (uh-prawk´-suh-mat)—To bring two tissue surfaces close together, as in the repair of a wound

Aseptic (a-sep´-tik)—Free from pathogens

Asexual (a-sek´-shuhl)—Relating to reproduction that does not involve the union of individual organisms or separate cells

Asymptomatic (a-sim{p}-tuh-mat´-ik)—Being without symptoms

Atomic (uh-tawm´-ik) **number**—The number of protons, or positive charges, in the nucleus of an atom of a particular element

Attenuated (uh-ten´-yuh-wat-uhd)—Weakened or lessened in power or effect

Bacteriocidin (bak-tir´-e-o-si-din)—A medication that kills bacteria

Base (bas´)—A substance that releases a hydroxide ion when dissolved

Basement membrane—The fragile, noncellular layer of tissue that secures the overlying layers of stratified epithelium

Bond (bawnd´)—The mechanism by which atoms link to one another to form molecules involving the loss of, gaining of, or sharing of electrons in the outer shell

Bursa (buhr´-suh)—A sac of synovial fluid that helps to reduce friction between a bone and tendon

Cardiac (kard´-e-ak)—Striated, involuntary muscle tissue that composes the walls of the heart

Carrier (kar´-e-uhr)—An organism capable of spreading disease

Cartilage (kart´-uhl-ij)—A type of body tissue that forms the skeleton of the developing fetus, most of which is converted to bone after birth

Catabolism (kuh-tab´-uh-liz-uhm)—The process of reducing large molecules into smaller molecules

Catalyst (kat´-uhl-uhst)—A substance that affects the rate of change in a chemical reaction without being changed chemically

Centrifuge (sen´-truh-fyuj)—A device that is used to separate the components of a solution or liquid mixture by spinning the substance

Cerebrospinal fluid (suh-re-bro-spin´-uhl flu´-uhd)—The tissue fluid that circulates around the brain and spinal cord

Cerumen (suh-ru´-muhn)—Ear wax, a secretion of the ceruminous glands in the ear canal

Chemical reaction (kem´-i-kuhl re-ak´-shuhn)—A process in which one or more chemicals that are exposed to other chemicals or sources of energy such as heat change their chemical composition to produce other chemicals and often other forms of energy

Colitis (ko-lit´-uhs)—An inflammatory condition of the large intestine characterized by severe diarrhea, bleeding, and ulceration of the mucosa of the intestine

Collagen (kawl´-uh-juhn)—A protein that composes strong fibers in several types of connective tissue

Concentration (kawn-sen-tra´-shuhn)—The ratio of the components of a solution or mixture

Congenital (kawn-jen´-uh-tuhl)—Present at birth as a result of conditions in the womb

Constrict (kuhn-strikt´)—To grow smaller or narrower

Contagious (kuhn-ta´-juhs)—Communicable, such as a disease that may be transmitted by direct or indirect contact

Convalescence (kawn-vuh-les´-uhns)—The process of a host's recovering from a disease

Coronal (kuh-ron′-uhl) **plane**—A lengthwise plane running from side to side and dividing the body into front and back parts

Cyst (sist′)—A capsule that forms around microorganisms before they enter dormant periods

Deep fascia (dep′ fash′-uh)—A band of connective tissue that covers or binds together body structures within body cavities

Dehiscence (di-his′-uhns)—The separation of the layers of a surgical wound

Dermis (duhr′-muhs)—The inner layer of skin consisting of papillary and reticular layers and containing blood and lymphatic vessels, nerves and nerve endings, glands, and hair follicles

Diffusion (dif-yu′-zhuhn)—The process of a substance moving from an area of high concentration to an area of lower concentration

Dilate (di-lat′)—To grow larger or expand

Disease (diz-ez′)—A specific illness or disorder characterized by a recognizable set of signs and symptoms and attributable to heredity, infection, diet, or environment

Disinfectant (dis-uhn-fek′-tuhnt)—A chemical used to destroy or reduce the growth of pathogens on objects

Elective (i-lek′-tiv) **procedure**—An operation done by choice as opposed to being performed as an emergency

Electron (i-lek′-trawn)—A negatively charged elementary particle of an atom

Endocardium (en-duh-kard′-e-uhm)—The lining of the heart chambers

Energy (en′-uhr-je)—The capacity to do work

Enteric (en-ter′-ik)—Pertaining to the intestine

Enzyme (en′-zim)—A protein that acts as a catalyst in a chemical reaction

Epidermis (ep-uh-duhr′-muhs)—The outer layer of skin made up of an outer, dead portion and a deeper, living, cellular portion

Epithelium (ep-uh-the′-le-uhm)—The covering of the internal organs of the body, also the lining of the vessels, body cavities, glands, and organs

Eustachian tube (yu-sta′-she-uhn tub′)—A canal that allows air to pass between the middle-ear cavity and the nasopharyngeal cavity

Eventration (e-vuhn-tra′-shuhn)—The partial protrusion of the abdominal contents through an opening in the abdominal wall

Evisceration (i-vis-uh-ra′-shuhn)—The extrusion of internal organs or viscera through a dehiscence

Examination (ig-zam-uh-na´-shuhn)—An evaluation of a person's health based on appearance, the person's feelings and behavior, and the status of indicators of health such as temperature, blood pressure, and body chemistry

Exhalation (eks-huh-la´-shuhn)—The act of breathing out or exhaling

Exoskeleton (ek-so-skel´-uht-uhn)—A characteristic of some organisms in which the outer tissue of parts of the body are hardened to the point that they support attached softer tissues

Extrinsic (ek-strin´-zik)—Outside of and not part of (the body)

Exudate (ek´-shu-dat)—A substance that has oozed from a body, such as from a cell

Facultative (fak´-uhl-tat-iv)—Having the ability to adapt to more than one condition

Fatal (fat´-uhl)—Resulting in death

Fever (fe´-vuhr)—An abnormally high body temperature

Fibrin (fi´-bruhn)—A stringy, insoluble protein produced in the clotting process

Fibrinogen (fi-brin´-uh-juhn)—A protein produced by the liver that is converted into fibrin by thrombin to promote clotting at an injury site

Fibroblast (fib´-ruh-blast)—A flat, elongated cell in the connective tissue that produces collagen and elastin fibers

Filament (fil´-uh-muhnt)—A threadlike, flexible structure

Fomite (fo´-mit)—An inanimate object that is contaminated with pathogens and is capable of transmitting pathogens to a human host

Gas (gas´)—A state of matter in which the substance will take on the shape of any container in which it is placed and will expand to fill the container

Genetic code (juh-net´-ik kod´)—The sequence of bases in DNA that determines how the organism will be structured

Genitourinary (jen-uh-to-yur´-uh-ner-e)—Referring to the structures and processes associated with urinary functions and reproduction

Giardiasis (je-ar-di´-uh-suhs)—A condition of diarrhea caused by drinking water containing giardia

Gland (gland´)—Any of the various structures within the body that produce specific chemicals to help with the functions of the body

Granulation (gran-yuh-la´-shuhn) **tissue**—Any soft, pink, fleshy projections that form during the healing process in a wound not healing by first intention

Heparin (hep´-uh-ruhn)—A chemical that helps prevent abnormal blood clotting

Histamine (his´-tuh-men)—A chemical that makes capillaries more permeable

Host (host´)—The organism that provides the resources required to sustain a parasitic relationship; an organism that serves as a permanent or temporary home for another organism

Humoral (hum´-uh-ruhl)—Referring to the old concept of the body having four basic humors or fluids, including the plasma in which humoral-immunity development takes place

Hydroxyl (hi-drawk´-suhl)—An anion consisting of one hydrogen atom and one oxygen atom

Hypodermis (hi-puh-duhr´-muhs)—The layer of areolar tissue and fat that lies beneath the dermis

Immune serum (im-yun´ sir´-uhm)—A serum that is taken from another organism (animal or human) and that contains antibodies against a specific disease

Immunity (im-yu´-nuht-e)—The state of being protected from the effects of a pathogen, generally due to having received a vaccination or because of the body's production of antibodies from a previous exposure to the organism

Inanimate (in-an´-uh-muht)—Nonliving

Incision (in-sizh´-uhn)—A smooth-sided wound, especially one made during surgery

Infestation (in-fes-ta´-shuhn)—The presence of parasites in the environment, on the skin, or in the hair of a host

Inflammation (in-fluh-ma´-shuhn)—A group of reactions exhibited by tissue when exposed to irritants; the reactions may include swelling, heat, pain, and other signs of irritation

Inflammatory response (in-flam´-uh-tor-e ri-spawns´)—The way the body reacts to an injury

Invertebrate (in-vuhrt´-uh-brat)—An organism that does not have an internal skeleton and, specifically, a spinal column

Involuntary—Muscles that work automatically

Ion (i´-awn)—An atom or group of atoms with either a positive or a negative electrical charge

Kinin (ki´-nuhn)—A polypeptide hormone that forms in the tissues and has its chief effect on smooth muscle

Lesion (le´-zhuhn)—A separation in tissue

Leukocyte (lu´-kuh-site)—another term for a white blood cell

Ligament (lig´-uh-muhnt)—A fibrous connective tissue that joins one bone to another

Liquid (lik´-wuhd)—A state of matter in which the substance will take on the shape of a container but will not expand to fill a container with greater volume than the substance

Lubricate (lu´-bruh-kat)—To improve the ease of movement between two objects by applying a substance that reduces friction

Lysis (li´-suhs)—A process of disintegration or dissolution (as of cells)

Lysosome (li´-suh-som)—A particle that contains digestive enzymes and hydrogen peroxide that chemically dissolve an engulfed pathogen

Lysozyme (li´-suh-zim)—An enzyme with antiseptic actions that destroys some foreign organisms

Malaria (muh-ler´-e-uh)—A parasitic infection of red blood cells by plasmodium virus transmitted by the bite of certain species of mosquito

Marrow (mar´-o)—The inner structure of most large bones

Matter (mat´-uhr)—That portion of the universe that has shape and substance

Median plane (med´-e-uhn plan´)—A lengthwise plane running through the midline of the body from front to back and dividing the body into equal right and left halves

Membrane (mem´-bran)—A thin layer of tissue that covers a surface, lines a cavity, or divides a space

Myocardium (mi-uh-kard´-e-uhm)—The thick middle layer of the heart wall

Neutron (nu´-trawn)—An elementary particle that is a fundamental component of the nucleus of atoms; it has no electric charge

Nonpurulent (nawn-pyur´-uh-luhnt)—Without pus

No-touch passing—Passing an object so that neither the person handing nor the person taking the object touches the object near a cutting edge

Nucleus (nu´-kle-uhs)—The structure in the center of an atom consisting of protons and neutrons and about which electrons orbit

Nutrient (nu´-tre-uhnt)—A substance that can be processed by the digestive system and used by the cells to produce energy or build tissue

Oblique (o-blek´) **plane**—A lengthwise plane passing through the body at a 45-degree angle to a sagittal plane or to the median plane

Organ (or´-guhn)—A special structure within the body that is arranged in an organized manner to perform a specific function

Organic compound (or-gan´-ik kawm-paund´)—A compound that contains carbon and hydrogen

Organism (or´-guh-niz-uhm)—A living person, animal, or plant

Parietal (puh-ri´-uht-uhl)—Of or pertaining to the outer wall of a cavity or organ

Pathogen (ath´-uh-juhn)—An organism that is capable of producing disease in another organism

Perforated (puhr´-fuh-rat-uhd) **organ**—An organ punctured in such a way that the contents of the organ could exude onto other structures

Pericardium (per-uh-kard´-e-uhm)—A sac that surrounds the heart

Perineum (per-uh-ne´-uhm)—The area of tissue behind the pelvis that gives passage to the urinary and genital ducts and to the rectum

Peritoneum (per-uht-uhn-e´-uhm)—An extensive serous membrane that covers the entire abdominal wall of the body

Permeability (puhr-me-uh-bil´-uht-e)—The characteristic of a material to allow other substances to pass through it

Permeable (puhr´-me-uh-buhl)—Capable of allowing substances to penetrate a structure

Phagocyte (fag´-uh-site)—A cell within the body that destroys invading organisms b engulfing and surrounding them

Platelet (plat´-luht)—A blood cell that helps the clotting process used to seal a wound

Pore (por´)—An opening in a surface that allows materials to pass through

Postoperative (po-stawp´-uh-ruht-iv)—Following a surgical procedure

Primary (pri´-mer-e) **union**—The situation in which severed tissue is essentially reunited with the tissue from which it was originally separated and that the healing process begins without disruptions from swelling, contamination, infection, and other factors

Protective reflex (pruh-tek´-tiv re´-fleks)—Coughing, sneezing, vomiting, tearing of the eyes, or other action that provides protection against pathogens

Proton (pro´-tawn)—A positively charged particle that is a fundamental component of the nucleus of atoms

Protoplasm (prot´-uh-plaz-uhm)—The complex mass of proteins and other organic and inorganic materials that is capable of exhibiting the characteristics of life

Pseudopod (sud´-uh-pawd)—An extension of the surface of a phagocyte; a "false foot"

Purulent (pyur´-uh-luhnt)—Containing pus

Respiration (res-puh-ra´-shuhn)—The physical and chemical processes by which an organism supplies its cells and tissues with oxygen and removes carbon dioxide

Rubor (ru´-bor)—The medical term for redness

Sagittal (saj´-uht-uhl) **plane**—A lengthwise plane running parallel to the median plane but not through the midline and dividing the body into unequal left and right parts

Salt (sawlt´)—A class of chemicals that have a positive ion other than hydrogen and a negative ion that is not a hydroxyl

Saturation point (sach-uh-ra´-shuhn point´)—The concentration level of a solution above which no more of a substance will dissolve

Scar (skar´)—A mark left on the skin as a result of an injury

Self-replication (self´ rep-luh-ka´-shuhn)—To produce a copy of oneself

Sensitized (sen´-suh-tizd)—Capable of being affected by a specific stimulus

Serous (sir´-uhs)—Epithelial tissue that lines closed body cavities and covers the organs in that cavity

Sexual (sek´-shuhl)—Relating to reproduce that requires a union of two organisms or the union of separate cells

Sexual maturation (sek´-shuhl mach-uh-ra´-shuhn)—The process of developing secondary sexual characteristics and becoming able to reproduce

Sharps (sharps´)—Instruments such as scalpels, needles, tweezers, and other devices that are capable of separating flesh; also includes foreign bodies such as glass, metal fragments, splinters, knives, and other objects that may be removed from the body and then present hazards to health-care workers

Sheath (sheth´)—A covering, especially a loose-fitting one

Shell (shel´)—The set of electron orbits in an atom that have the same energy level

Skeletal (skel´-uht-uhl)—Striated, voluntary muscle tissue attached to bones

Solid (sawl´-uhd)—A state of matter in which the substance has a definite shape that is maintained unless acted upon by a force that is capable of changing that shape

Spore (spor´)—The dormant form of a bacterium or the reproductive form of a fungus

Sputum (sp{y}ut´-uhm)—Substance expelled from the respiratory tract that may contain mucus, pus, cellular materials, blood, and other materials

Sterilize (ster´-uh-liz)—To destroy all of the pathogens on an object or in a substance

Striated (stri´-at-uhd)—Lined with grooves

Structure (struhk´-chuhr)—A part of the body, such as the heart, a bone, a gland, a cell, or a limb

Subdermal (suhb-duhr´-muhl)—Below the skin

Surgery (sur´-juhre)—A medical procedure intended to correct physical defects, repair injuries, or treat diseases, especially through the use of medical instruments

Susceptibility (suh-sep-tuh-bil´-uht-e)—The degree to which a person is likely to contract a disease

Suture (su´-chuhr)—A stitch placed in tissue to hold the sides of a wound together during the healing process

Symptom (sim{p}´-tuhm)—A condition that occurs in association with a disease and that can be evidence of the presence of the disease

System (sis´-tuhm)—A group of organs and related structures that work together to perform a common function

Tendon (ten´-duhn)—A fibrous connective tissue that connects muscle to bones

Tensile strength (ten´-sil stren{k}th´)—A material's resistance to being torn apart by opposing forces

Theory (the´-uh-re)—A statement that provides an explanation based on evidence without final proof being obtained

Theory of evolution (ev-uh-lu´-shuhn)—A theory that proposes that all life began as simple organic compounds that over time developed the characteristics of life and continued to become more complex in functioning and in coping with the environment

Toxin (tawk´-suhn)—A substance that is harmful to cells

Toxoid (tawk´-soid)—A toxin that has been modified so as not to be harmful

Trachea (tra´-ke-uh)—The windpipe

Transverse (tranz´-vuhrs) **plane**—A horizontal plane passing through the body from front to back and dividing the body into equal upper and lower parts

Trauma (trau´-muh)—An injury to living tissue caused by an extrinsic agent

Umbilicus (uhm-buh-li´-kuhs)—The point at which the umbilical cord joined the fetus to the mother's womb during pregnancy; commonly referred to as the *navel* or *belly button*

Unicellular (yu-ni-sel´-yuh-luhr)—Consisting of one cell

Vaccination (vak-suh-na´-shuhn)—The administration of a medication that increases the body's resistance to a specific pathogen

Vaccine (vak´-sen)—A suspension of diluted or killed microorganisms administered in order to stimulate the production of antibodies to promote an active immunity to that pathogen

Vectors (vek´-tuhrs) **of disease**—The conditions that tend to promote the spread of a disease, such as when the bite of an arthropod allows pathogens to enter a person's bloodstream

Venipuncture (ven´-uh-puhn{k}-chuhr)—A procedure that involves puncturing a vein

Visceral (vis´-uh-ruhl)—Smooth, involuntary muscle tissue that lines the walls of hollow organs; of or pertaining to the viscera, or internal organs in the abdominal cavity

Vitality (vi-tal´-uht-e)—The ability to carry out life functions efficiently

Vital organ (vit´-uhl or´-guhn)—An organ that must function properly in order for the life of the organism to continue

Voluntary (vawl´-uhn-ter-e)—Muscles that are consciously controlled by the will of a person

Zoonosis (zo-uh-no´-suhs)—A disease of animals that is transmissible to humans from its primary animal host